THE *Royal Doulton®*
GREAT GENERALS
COLLECTION
General Gordon
D 6869
SECOND IN A SERIES OF 10
DESIGNED AND MODELLED BY

A Special Edition of 1,500
Produced by Royal Doulton for U.K. International Ceramics
© 1990 ROYAL DOULTON

Royal Doulton®
LEPRECHAUN
D 6899
Modelled by

© 1989 ROYAL DOULTON
SPECIALLY COMMISSIONED FROM
ROYAL DOULTON
IN AN EDITION SIZE OF 500

the sign of
the green

FALSTAFF
D 6795
Modelled by
H. FENTON
© 1948 ROYAL DOULTON
NEW COLOURWAY 1987

In Record of the First Canadian Doulton Show in Durham, Ontario, July 1988 Special Edition of 750

Royal Doulton®
YACHTSMAN
D 6820
Modelled by

© 1988 ROYAL DOULTON

GREETINGS
CLIFF CORNELL

"FAMOUS CORNELL FLUXES"
CLEVELAND FLUX COMPANY

INTERNATIONAL COLLECTORS CLUB
ROYAL DOULTON

D 6656
JOHN DOULTON
1793 - 1873
**EXCLUSIVELY FOR
COLLECTORS CLUB**
© ROYAL DOULTON
TABLEWARE LTD. 1980

© ROYAL DOULTON TABLEWARE LIMITED 1983
D 6710

**THE
CELEBRITY
COLLECTION**
by Royal Doulton
A hand-made, hand-decorated series
GROUCHO MARX ⊖
"I've worked myself up
from nothing to a state
of extreme poverty"

Groucho Marx ⊖

Original Concept by Kevin Pearson and Geoff Blower

Royal Doulton®
THE COLLECTOR
D 6796
Modelled by

A Special Edition of 5000
From "The Collecting World" series
Produced by Royal Doulton
for Kevin Francis Ceramics
© 1987 ROYAL DOULTON
AND KEVIN FRANCIS CERAMICS
THE COLLECTOR

SOUVENIR FROM BENTALLS
V.I
N°h 70006
1936.

Royal Doulton®
SANTA CLAUS
D 6668
Modelled by

SPECIAL EDITION SIZE OF 1,000
© 1988 ROYAL DOULTON

American Collectors Society

First in the series
Journey Through Britain
THE POSTMAN
D 6801
Issued in a limited edition
of 5000
Modelled by Stanley J. Taylor
The POST OFFICE and ROYAL MAIL
are trade marks of the Post Office
Reproduced under licence
© 1988 Royal Doulton

This is no.

Royal Doulton®
JOHN BARLEYCORN
TANKARD
D 6788
*Specially Commissioned
by*
AMERICAN EXPRESS
Modelled by

© 1987 ROYAL DOULTON

Collecting Royal Doulton Character & Toby Jugs

THE DIAMOND JUBILEE
1934-1994
A RECORD OF THE FIRST SIXTY YEARS

COMPILED BY

Jocelyn Lukins

THIRD EDITION

FOR BILL HARPER

ACKNOWLEDGMENTS

I gratefully acknowledge here all the collectors and dealers who have allowed me to photograph pieces in their collections and those who have loaned me photographs, including Valerie Baynton, Bill Cross, Fred Dearden, Dan Downie, Katherine Ellis, Kevin Francis, Neil Galatz, John Haggart, Louise Irvine, Peter Jones, Tony Kenny, Elizabeth Nevell, Mark Oliver, Doug Pinchin, Jamie Pole, Frank Savage, Leah Selig, John Sinclair, Nick Tzimas, Bea Vitkovitch, Yesterdays

I am indebted to *Royal Doulton* for a very generous loan of photographs and for producing the pieces which are the subject of this book.

The name *Doulton* and *Royal Doulton* and the backstamps shown are *registered trade marks*.

The opinions expressed are very much my own.

© Jocelyn Lukins 1994

I.S.B.N.0 9510288 71

First Published 1985
Second Edition 1989
Third Edition 1994

Published by Venta Books

Photography by Jocelyn Lukins.
David Westcott. Tom Power.

Designed by Pep Reiff

Set by Cassandra Moulen

Printed by Bookmag, Inverness

JOCELYN LUKINS photography Ventafile

The majority of photographs and illustrations in this book have been supplied by Ventafile, a compilation of material and information assembled by Jocelyn Lukins.

INTRODUCTION

In 1806, the year after he started his apprenticeship as a potter in Lambeth, John Doulton took his only day's holiday that year to attend the funeral of Admiral Lord Nelson at St.

Paul's Cathedral. It is appropriate that the Nelson jug became, as early as the 1820s, the first character jug made by Doulton. John Doulton probably enjoyed producing something a little more interesting than the hundreds of stoneware utilitarian bottles, his usual day's output. Doulton and Watts showed a Nelson jug at the Great Exhibition in Hyde Park, London in 1851.

They made three versions – the head and shoulders model shown here in three sizes, of which a replica of the medium size was produced in 1905, the Centenary of the Battle of Trafalgar; a jug modelled to the waist; and another similar which formed a large flask. About this time the first toby jugs were produced by the firm. They were modelled on a traditional English form showing a seated man astride a barrel of ale. That it is strong ale is shown by the double X marking. The drinker was known as a 'toper' from the French word *tope* = to toast, and this in turn gave its name to the toby jug. So in these very early days we already have the forerunners of the present day popular collectables.

Through the Lambeth years, toby jugs were designed by many of their leading artists. About 1912 Leslie Harradine produced the first Dickens character in his Pecksniff jug, a Highwayman, Theodore Roosevelt and Old King Cole, forerunners of the Burslem titles. The Lambeth artist whose influence on the Burslem collection is strongest however, was Harry Simeon

1894-1936, whose toby jugs, teapots and tobacco jars have their equivalents in the later range.

Pecksniff jug 7.5 in. Designed by Leslie Harradine, Lambeth *c.* 1912

If you compare the photograph of Harry Simeon's Lambeth toby c1925 and *The Best is not too Good* D6107 adapted from it by Harry Fenton in 1939, you will see how much is owed to these forerunners.

At the Doulton Burslem factory other precursors of the present range were appearing. The Huntsman toby D6320 introduced into the range in 1950 had originally made its appearance in 1919. The *Charlie* design was registered in 1918. *George Robey* was commissioned 1925. Kingsware Versions of *The Huntsman* D6320 and *The Squire* D6319 were made pre-1940. All the above are tobies, full length figures which carried on the traditions of the eighteenth century jugs. There have always been figural jugs throughout history but the English tradition of the toby jug and its connection with drinking must have been very familiar to Charles Noke whose father was an antique dealer in Worcester. However it was his creation, the character jug, which showed the head only and gave great scope for fine modelling which showed such genius.

The Huntsman D4090 8 in. Bright orange coat and yellow waistcoat. Burslem. Silver rim Hallmark for 1919

D6320 *The Huntsman* 7 in. Kingsware Burslem c. 1940

Charles Noke, the Art Director of the Doulton Burslem factory produced his double-faced *Janus* figures as early as the 1890s and they included a range of matchstrikers. It was not until 1937 that he introduced the character jug of *Mephistopheles*, so clearly derived from one of these. Noke's first character in the range, *John Barleycorn*, was based on a very early traditional English form potted by many factories.

The characters of the 1930s were traditional subjects like *Old Charley*, the watchman, *Simon the Cellarer*, *Parson Brown* and *Auld Mac* and *Paddy*, the archetypal Scotsman and Irishman.

John Peel became the first real person to be depicted in 1936, with Churchill the first contemporary person in 1940.

D6319 The Squire Kingsware.6 in, Burslem c. 1940.

It is indeed a claim to fame to have one's likeness perpetuated in a Doulton character jug in one's lifetime, as were the Beatles, Ronald Reagan, Michael Doulton, and Status Quo.

In sixty years, characters from legend and history, fact and fiction have joined the band of faces and from the following list the collector can make a choice.

Harvest jug 7.5 in. (19cm). Made for a whisky distiller by the Martin Bros, London c. 1890.

Two faced *Mephistopheles* matchstriker 2.5 in. Designed by Noke, Burslem 1880s

V

CAPTAIN AHAB
Designed by Garry Sharpe

D6500	Large	1959-1985
D6506	Small	1959-1985
D6522	Mini	1960-1985
D6505	Table Lighter	1964-1973

Captain Ahab, from *Moby Dick* (1851) by Herman Melville, is the captain of a whaler who has lost a leg in an attempt to capture Moby Dick, a particularly evasive and cunning white whale. The revengeful Captain Ahab pursues Moby Dick around the oceans until they engage in a thrilling contest which lasts three whole days. Moby Dick triumphs in the end, kills Captain Ahab, sinks his ship, the *Pequod*, and drowns all his crew except one, who is left to tell the terrible tale.

AMERICAN EXPRESS SPECIAL COMMISSION
JOHN BARLEYCORN Designed by Stan Taylor

D6780 Tankard 6in. 1988.

No. 12 in a collector's set of twelve tankards by various manufacturers. A promotional package offered to American Express card holders in the U.S.

W.C. FIELDS D6674 Large 1983. Limited Edition 1,500

MAE WEST D6688 Large 1983. Limited Edition 625

Backstamped *Premier edition for American Express*. These jugs were intended as a promotional offer for American Express card holders. The project was abandoned and the jug offered exclusively to U.S. *R.D.I.C.C.* members. Later in 1983 they entered the general range.

THE ANGLER
Designed by Stan Taylor. D6866 Small 1990 -
One of a series of 8 sporting subjects, all modelled by Stan Taylor and issued in the small size only in 1990 and 1991.

Angling, fishing with rod and line, is the most popular sport in Britain. If the fish stocks should run out at least half the pleasure will remain, of sitting on a river bank, away from all your troubles, communing with nature.

Fly fishing may be very pleasant amusement: but angling or float fishing can only compare to a stick and string, with a worm at one end and a fool at the other.

Attr. Samuel Johnson

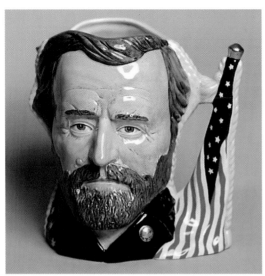

Royal Doulton
'The Antagonists'
Collection
D.6698
The Civil War
Ulysses S. Grant/Robert E. Lee
Hand made and Hand decorated
Designed by Michael Abberley

© COPYRIGHT ROYAL DOULTON TABLEWARE LIMITED 1982
Worldwide Limited Edition of 9,500

A series of four double-sided jugs on an American theme with the winning contestant taking the front position.

ULYSSES S. GRANT & ROBERT E. LEE

Designed by Michael Abberley
D6698 Large 1983
No. 1 in the collection.

Worldwide limited editions of 9,500. Special backstamp for 'The Antagonists' Collection'. Each jug with facsimile signature of the designer and numbered.

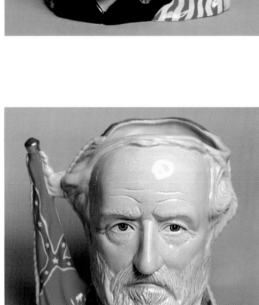

Grant was a natural soldier with iron courage and a thorough knowledge of the practice of fighting. He rose quickly through the ranks to become chief of the Union armies of the North in the American Civil War (1861-1865). Even so, he was outmanoeuvred by his adversary, Lee who commanded the Confederate forces and was a great strategist. However, the brave 'Lion of the South' was eventually cornered and, with an exhausted and diminishing army, he had no alternative but to surrender.

CHIEF SITTING BULL & GEORGE ARMSTRONG CUSTER

Designed by Michael Abberley
D6712   Large   1984

No. 2 in the collection.

Chief Sitting Bull and General George Armstrong Custer were adversaries in the Battle of Little Big Horn, 24 June 1876. Sitting Bull was Chief of the Sioux Indians, whose formerly guaranteed reservations were being threatened by the flood of white men in search of gold in the Dakota Hills. General Custer led a column of U.S. Cavalry sent to protect the white man's interests, thus giving rise to a difficult situation with no solution, but disaster. An over-confident and uninformed Custer led his 266 men into action without waiting for reinforcements and found himself grossly outnumbered by the Sioux warriors. Sitting Bull is shown as the victor in the conflict and placed on the forward side of this jug.

SANTA ANNA & DAVY CROCKETT

Designed by Michael Abberley
D6729   Large   1985

No. 3 in the collection.

The Alamo was originally a Spanish fortified mission. European colonialists settled the Spanish lands north of the Rio Grande and there were frequent clashes between the two nationalities. A detachment of Americans occupied the Alamo in 1835 and were besieged there by 5,000 troops under command of the Mexican General, Santa Anna. After twelve days, on 6th March 1836, he captured the fortress. Allowing the women and children safe conduct, he massacred the 180 men. Amongst the brave defenders were English, an Irishman, Scotsmen, Welshmen, one Dane and representatives of most of the American States. The fortress ruins, which form the handle of this jug, are now a National Monument to them.

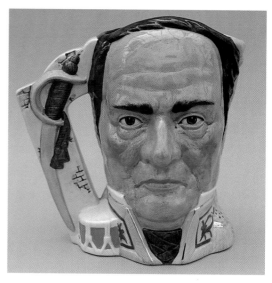

One of their number was Davy Crockett (1786-1836) who was a remarkable hunter from Tennessee. He once killed forty-seven bears in a month although he also kept tame ones. He killed Indians, but also was their friend. He was a whisky-swilling extrovert and, as the song about him says 'King of the Wild Frontier'

Antonio Lopez de Santa Anna, two months after his victory at the Alamo and with 1400 crack troops under his command, was opposed by General Sam Houston at the San Jacinto river in southern Texas. The roughly trained Texans were outnumbered two to one, but in the ensuing fight, only seven were killed. The Mexicans lost 600 men and Santa Anna was taken prisoner. After only twelve months he was released and sent back to Mexico, but Texas had been gained for the Union.

4

GEORGE WASHINGTON & GEORGE III

Designed by Michael Abberley
D6749   Large   1986

No. 4 in the collection.

George III reigned fifty-nine years, and had nine sons and six daughters. He loved having his family around him. He was musical, liked good books, mending watches, and making buttons. He was a keen gardener and was interested in the latest developments in agriculture. He had all the attributes of a country squire and his subjects fondly referred to him as 'Farmer George', hence the wagon wheel and the pitchfork on the handle. However, as king he was autocratic and obstinate and particularly clumsy in handling his North American colonies.

Those whom he referred to as the *rebels* found the perfect leader in George Washington. He might have been a country gentleman from Virginia, but his talents as a military commander were needed. He was a strong opponent of British policies. He led his largely untrained recruits against superior forces and used them to maximum effect. He brought them to victory and independence.

In peace, Washington remained a leader and became the first president of the Republic of the United States. His side of the handle is formed by the Declaration of Independence, a quill and an ink pot.

JOHNNY APPLESEED

Designed by Harry Fenton
D6372   Large   1953-1969

'Johnny Appleseed' was the nickname of John Chapman, (1776-1847) a New Englander who has become a pioneer hero in the United States of America. A true frontiersman he planted apple pips near settlers' cabins, and tending the trees for others to enjoy the fruit. He was friendly with the Indians.

A vegetarian, all animals were his friends. He once refused to kill a hornet which stung him. He thought pruning and grafting, a cruelty to the tree. He became a follower of the Swedenborg philosophy. Harry Fenton has done his research well, reproducing the scanty beard he was described as having and the gentle goodness of his face. The handle is formed by an apple branch and leather haversack. There is a New Testament on the reverse.

'ARD OF 'EARING'

Designed by David Biggs
D6588   Large   1964-1967
D6591   Small   1964-1967
D6594   Mini   1964-1967

This wily, rather Dickensian character cups his ear with his hand and complains of his being 'ard of 'earing. One feels that if one offered him a glass of ale he might hear very well. David Biggs had a very clever idea for a jug handle here. However, being of a rather unattractive type, the jug did not sell well, had a short production run, and has since become very rare and desirable.

'ARRY AND 'ARRIET are Cockney characters, the true Londoners, born within the sound of Bow Bells – the bells of the church of St. Mary-le-Bow in the City of London. They have a characteristic Cockney dialect which includes many dropped aichs, and a language of rhyming slang all their own, such as when 'Arry refers to 'Arriet as 'My old China' (china plate, rhyming with mate).

'ARRIET

Designed by Harry Fenton

D6208	Large	1947-1960
D6236	Small	1947-1960
D6250	Mini	1947-1960
D6256	Tiny	1947-1969

PEARLY GIRL

Large and Small sizes – 1946

A very rare variation of 'Arriet with different colourations, notably a blue jacket with a red or gold scarf and red/maroon or lime green and pink hat on dark brown hair. Unlike the other rare variations, *Pearly Boy* and Girl seemed to have commenced production after the war in 1946. *Pearly Boy* with brown buttons occurs in quite large numbers but *Pearly Girl* is very rare indeed. Unlike the pilot jugs all these rare variations were sold retail.

Whereas Doulton always referred to these jugs as "'*Arry* and '*Arriet* with buttons", collectors invented the titles "*Pearly Girl and Boy*" which are now common usage.

'ARRY

Designed by Harry Fenton

D6207	Large	1947-1960
D6235	Small	1947-1960
D6249	Mini	1947-1960
D6255	Tiny	1947-1960

"PEARLY BOY"

Large, Small and Mini sizes

This is a rare variation of 'Arry with the addition of moulded pearl buttons on the cap and collar, and has in turn four colour variations:

Brown hat, Blue coat & White buttons.
Brown hat, Brown coat & White buttons.
Brown hat, Brown coat & Brown buttons.
Beige hat, Brown coat & White buttons.

Doulton registered a design for 'Arry c. 1942 with the suggested cockney expletive *Blimey!* on the reverse. This corruption of an earlier oath *God Blind Me!* was probably considered unsuitable at a very early stage and the design was not produced.

8

AULD MAC (OWD MAC)

Designed by Harry Fenton

D5823	Large	1937-1986
D5824	Small	1937-1987
D6253	Mini	1945-1987
D6257	Tiny	1946-1960
D5889	Musical Jug	1938-c. 1939
D6006	Ash Bowl	1938-1960

Jugs dated 1937 are found with *Owd Mac* incised on the hat. This changed in 1938 to *Auld Mac*. However, the backstamp remained as *Owd Mac* until 1942. Auld Mac is the archetypal Scotsman. On the reverse of the jug is the legend, *Bang went saxpence*, being a phrase from a song sung by Sir Harry Lauder, a Scots comedian and famous music-hall star of the early twentieth century. The song tells of Mac's visit to London when, every time he turned round, bang went sixpence. Times have not changed for the better! There is a Lambeth stoneware flask, made for Dewars, with a caricature by Dudley Hardy of Sir Harry Lauder.

BACCHUS

Designed by Max Henk

D6499	Large	1959-1991
D6505	Small	1959-1991
D6521	Mini	1960-1991
D6505	Table Lighter	1964-1973

Early variations of the miniature size are found with vine leave on the handle which do not appear on the later examples. Bacchus was the Roman God of Wine. The Bacchanalia, which the Romans celebrated in his honour, became such orgies of licentiousness that they were banned in 186 B.C. The celebrations took place at the time of the grape harvest, and he is shown here crowned with vines and with a jaunty bunch of grapes over one ear.

9

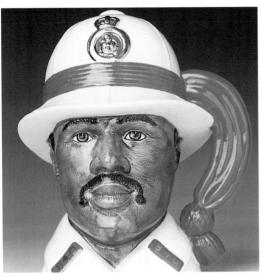

BAHAMAS POLICEMAN
Designed by Bill Harper
D6912   Large   1992

Limited Edition of 1,000

Commissioned by Island Galleria
International Bazaar, Freeport,
Bahamas.
Special Gold backstamp.

This jug was based on a photograph of
the local policeman AB 840 whose
beat included *"The Island Galleria"*, a
china and glass store owned by Mr.
Paul Lane who commissioned it.

Artistic licence meant that a pith
helmet, already obsolete in 1992 was
used and the pink ribbon hat band was changed to red for greater effect.

This jug has the same design number as *The Snake Charmer*.

JOHN BARLEYCORN
Designed by Charles Noke

D5327	Large	1934-1960
D5735	Small	1937-1960
D5735	Mini	1939-1960
D6952	Tiny	1994
D5602	Ash Tray	1936-1960
D5327	Large	1978-1982

John Barleycorn is the personification
of barley, from which malt liquor is
made. His face has become flattened
by being ground between the
millstones and he has the merry grin
associated with alcoholic beverages.

Introduced in 1934 this was the first
jug in the range. It is closer to the early
English harvest jugs, than any other, and similar to the 'face jugs' produced by the Martin
Brothers (1870-1920). At first the handle led inside the rim of the jug, and this is the rarer
version, 1934-1939. Remodelled by Michael Abberley, a special exhibition reproduction
limited to 7,500. Sold at Royal Doulton Special Events, first in North America in 1978 and
until 1982 worldwide. It is distinguished by a black handle and a special back stamp.

See Diamond Jubilee tinies.
See American Express commissions.

10

BASEBALL PLAYER

Designed by David Biggs
A Pilot jug.

A Large size jug in the same series as the Golfer, the Jockey and the Yachtsman. All designed by David Biggs in the early '70s and each with a very distinctive handle. Two colourways exist, one in red and the other blue.

Baseball is the national game of the United States of America. It is played by teams of nine players a side who take it in turns to bat on a diamond-shaped field. The laws of baseball are extremely complicated and there are over a hundred rules. Baseball players are national heroes, and the team scores are as avidly followed as the state of the stock market or the political parties.

'Baseball is an island of surety in a changing world' Bill Veeck.

SITE OF THE GREEN
Toronto Blue Jay
Small 1994
Limited Edition 2,500
Special Backstamp.

BASEBALL PLAYER
SECOND VERSION
Designed by Stan Taylor
D6878   Small   1991
Issued only in the USA

Commemorative Issues.
BRITANNIA LTD.
DOULTON CONVENTION
Florida Show January 1991
Special Edition of 500 with Special Backstamp.

STRAWBRIDGE AND CLOTHIER
To celebrate 125th anniversary.
D6957 Small   Nov. 1993
Special Colourway.
Red cap and red striped uniform of *The Philadelphia "Phillies"*.
Limited edition of 250.

No doubt as with the *Football Supporter* jug other teams will be represented.

Royal Doulton
THE BEATLES
Paul McCartney
D 6724
Modelled by

Stanley James Taylor.

© ROYAL DOULTON TABLEWARE
LIMITED 1984

THE BEATLES

Designed by Stan Taylor

D6724	Paul McCartney
	1984-1991
D6725	John Lennon
	1984-1991
D6726	Ringo Starr
	1984-1991
D6727	George Harrison
	1984-1991

| D6797 | John Lennon   Mid Size |
| | 1988 |

See Special Commissions – Sinclair.

First issued in Liverpool in July 1984. Available in the rest of the U.K. in August 1984. Not for sale in the U.S.A. for copyright reasons. These jugs are made in a 'Fine China' body in a mid size – 5.5in. 14 cm.

Special Backstamp *1991 Final Year of Issue*

This group was first formed in Liverpool. In the early 1960s it consisted of George Harrison (lead guitar), John Lennon (rhythm guitar), Paul McCartney (bass guitar) and Ringo Star (drums). Lennon and McCartney were also responsible for many of the melodies and lyrics which soon caught the world in their spell, and brought on a severe case of 'Beatlemania'.

Their musicianship and versatility kept them at the top of the world's charts and brought them fame and fortune. Fans followed their adventures in the cinema and in real life around the world reading avidly any detail of their personal lives which could be discovered or invented. It was their music however with its sense of well being and warmth which gave them such lasting popularity with the teeny boppers and grannies alike.

The golden boys split up in the '70s to follow their own pursuits but the tracks they recorded together have taken on a timeless quality.

John Lennon was assassinated in New York in 1980.

12

BEEFEATER

Designed by Harry Fenton

D6206	Large	1947-
D6233	Small	1947-
D6251	Mini	1947-1992
D6806	Tiny	1988
D6233	Table Lighter	1958-1973

The Royal Cypher on the handle was changed from G.R. to E.R., in 1953, the year of Queen Elizabeth's Coronation. On early copies the crown, cypher and name are picked out in yellow until c.1949. The plural *Beefeaters* appears on the base of early models until c.1953.

Beefeater is the popular name given to the Yeoman of the Guard. It is a corruption of 'Buffetiers' which was a body of foot guards formed in the reign of Henry VII 1485-1509 for the protection of the Royal Person. They perform this duty on ceremonial occasions and still wear the style of dress worn in the Tudor period. They are all veteran warrant officers. Since 1986 this character has been included in the *London Collection* and a bright on-glaze red used.

See R.D.I.C.C. issues.

See *Yeoman of the Guard.*

BENTALLS LTD.

(London Department Stores)
Small size Character jugs are found overprinted on the base with special backstamps for Bentalls.

1. 'Souvenir from Bentalls Jubilee Year 1935'.
Old Charley, Parson Brown, Sairey Gamp, Tony Weller.

2. 'Souvenir from Bentalls 1936'
Jester, Simon the Cellarer, Dick Turpin, Old Charley.

CAPTAIN WILLIAM BLIGH

(1754-1817) accompanied Captain Cook on his second voyage of discovery in 1772. In 1787 he commanded H.M.S. BOUNTY on an expedition to the Pacific. This episode in his life has been much filmed and the mutiny of his crew and his being cast adrift with 18 others in an open boat is well known. He skillfully navigated a 4,000 miles journey and made landfall after 45 days. He was appointed Governor of New South Wales in 1811. The bully portrayed by Charles Laughton and Anthony Hopkins wasn't the whole story. The Bounty's voyage was to transport breadfruit trees from Tahiti to introduce them into the W. Indies. So that it is appropriate that his tomb is in the churchyard of St. Mary's, Lambeth. The church is now a Museum of gardening owned by The Trandescant Trust. It has two memorials by George Tinworth. One is set there by Sir Henry Doulton in memory of his wife, Sarah.

CHARACTER JUG OF THE YEAR 1995
BONNIE PRINCE CHARLIE

Designed by Stan Taylor
D6858   Large   1990-

Thistle of Scotland and Crown form the handle.

Charles wears the Royal Stuart Tartan and the white cockade adopted by his followers. Charles Edward Stuart 1720-1788, known as 'The Young Pretender'. Unsuccessfully tried to restore the Stuarts to the English throne, landing at Inverness in 1745 with 7 companions, his dash and charm were such that he entered Edinburgh with 2000 highlanders and progressed south through England as far as Derby before he withdrew to Scotland through lack of support. Disastrously defeated at Culloden in 1746 he wandered the highlands for five months with a price on his head. With the help of loyal supporters he escaped to France but the Stuart cause was lost forever.

BOWLS PLAYER

Designed by Stan Taylor
D6896   Small   1991-1994

Handle – bowl, jack and measure.

Bowls is yet another sport whose benefits include fresh air, exercise and pleasant company. It is very popular with the retired community. The play takes place on a velvety textured grass green. There are 1- 4 players who bowl their biased bowls as close to the white jack as possible.

THE BRITISH TOBY,
Toronto, Canada.

Alison and Dick Nicholson, with a retail shop selling Doulton, ran very successful International Royal Doulton Collectors weekends in Toronto. The highlights of these events were the auctioning of rare jugs such as *Terry Fox*, the prototype *Marilyn Monroe* and the pre-release of *The Ringmaster*, with the Maple Leaf backstamp (25th anniversary of Canadian flag), and the new issue of a set of three Canadian servicemen *"On Guard for Thee"*.

D6863 RINGMASTER LARGE 1990
Edition of 750
D6881 TERRY FOX LARGE 1990
Only 3 copies made
D6903/4/5 "ON GUARD FOR THEE" 1991
250 each of set of 3 small jugs
Prototype MARILYN MONROE 1993

PARSON BROWN

Designed by Charles Noke

D5486	Large	1935-1960
D5529	Small	1935-1960
D6955	Tiny	1994
D5600	Ash Tray	1936-1960
D6008	Ash Bowl	1939-1960

The clergyman was an important figure in country society. His 'living' included a comfortable parsonage a portion of tithes and offerings for his support from his parishioners. In return he preached his sermons, christened, married, comforted and buried his 'flock'. He was not always a solemn cleric – this parson looks a merry member of the community, as at home taking his ale in the local tavern as wine at the squire's table.

Found with fitted silver rim as is also *Simon the Cellarer*. This would be carried out by the retailer.

See Diamond Collection.

BUFFALO BILL

A large size prototype which escaped from the factory in the '70s.

The character was re-introduced into the range in *The Wild West* Series in 1985.

THE BUSKER

Designed by Stan Taylor
D6775   Large   1988-1991

Itinerant entertainers have always been a familiar sight on the London streets but in recent years they have multiplied. Every underground station has its musician and the Covent Garden Piazza has a continuous programme of musicians, jugglers and actors. The busker of this jug is an old-style character with his concertina handle. A prototype was made with a figural handle, a one-man-band.

From *The London Collection.*

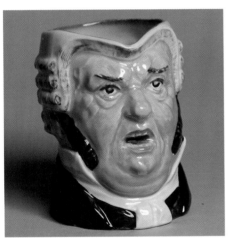

BUZ FUZ

Designed by Charles Noke with the later models by Harry Fenton

D5838	Mid Size	1938-1948
D5838	Small	1948-1960
D6048	Bust	1939-1960
D5838	Table Lighter	1958

The Mid-Size was not popular and scaled down from January 1st 1948.

Doulton spell *Buz Fuz* in two words, Dickens spelt it as one.

Buzfuz, from the *Pickwick Papers* (1836) by Charles Dickens, was Mrs. Bardell's counsel in the case of breach of promise she brought against Mr. Pickwick.

Serjeant Buzfuz then rose with all the majesty and dignity which the grave nature of the proceedings demanded ...pulled his gown over his shoulders, settled his wig, and addressed the jury.

CANADIAN CENTENNIAL 1867-1967

D6610	LUMBERJACK	Large	1967
D6611	NORTH AMERICAN		
	INDIAN	Large	1967
D6609	TRAPPER	Large	1967

These jugs are found overprinted with this special backstamp. They were sale only in North America in 1967.

CANADIAN CENTENNIAL SERIES
1867 – 1967

The Trapper
D 6609

16

CANADIAN ASSOCIATION OF ART AND COLLECTABLES SHOWS

YACHTSMAN

Designed by Stan Taylor
D6820   Large   1988
Special edition of 750 to commemorate the first
Canadian Doulton Show in July 1988. Entered the
general range in the same colourway in 1989.

GUY FAWKES

Designed by Bill Harper
D6861   Large   1990

Special edition of 750 to commemorate the third
annual *Canadian Collectables Showcase* in May
1990. A pre-release with a slight colour change –
an orange hat band rather than red.

Royal Doulton®
YACHTSMAN
D 6820
Modelled by
Stanley James Taylor
© 1988 ROYAL DOULTON

THE CARDINAL

Designed by Charles Noke
D5614   Large   1936-1960
D6033   Small   1939-1960
D6129   Mini   1940-1960
D6258   Tiny   1947-1960

Early versions have the embossed
title picked out in purple.

A dignitary of the Roman Catholic Church. This jug
bears a likeness to a vellum figure designed by
Charles Noke in the 1890s. It portrayed Henry
Irving as Cardinal Wolsey in Shakespeare's *Henry
VIII* and was later included in the H.N. range of
figurines.

LEWIS CARROLL

Charles Dodgson 1832-98, was a lecturer in mathematics at Oxford University and a pioneer of photography most but is most remembered for the popular nonsense stories he wrote for Alice Liddell, daughter of Dean Liddell, head of Dodgson's college, Christ Church. He wrote *Alice's Adventures in Wonderland* in 1865 and the sequel *Through the Looking Glass* in 1872. He was a shy bachelor with a stammer, yet his imaginative stories have a keen sense of fun and observation and are universally popular with young and old. The stories are full of references to Oxford life.

Doulton produced character jugs based on his stories in 1965. *Ugly Duchess and Mad Hatter* from *The Adventures in Wonderland* and *The Walrus and the Carpenter* from *Through the Looking Glass*. All three are discontinued. In 1987 Doulton commenced a new series of characters. '*The Red Queen*, a chess piece character from *Through the Looking Glass* but appearing as the Queen of Hearts, a playing card character from *Alice in Wonderland*. *The March Hare* from *Alice in Wonderland*, the first animal personality not portrayed as a handle and the *Cook and Cheshire Cat* from *Alice in Wonderland*. I hope in the future Doulton will use more of Carroll's amusing characters for Jugs. If you haven't read the books, do, and if you have, read them again, and maybe you can suggest some other characters.

THE CAVALIER

Designed by Harry Fenton
D6114   Large   1940-1960
D6173   Small   1941-1960

The *Cavalier* here, in his ostrich-plumed hat and ruff, is dressed as a Royalist in the English Civil War (1642-46). A cultivated gentleman, he is always ready to take up his sword and ride against King Charles's enemies to defend the good life which he knows so well how to enjoy.

Here's a health unto His Majesty with a fa-la-la, la, la, la, la. Confusion to his enemies, with a fa-la-la, la, la, la, la.   Traditional Song

CAVALIER WITH GOATEE. 1940-1950.

This jug was introduced at the outbreak of the Second World War and then sported a goatee-beard in deference to the fashion set by Charles I. This type could have continued until 1950 when mould changes to the collar are mentioned and clearly shown here. Another noticeable variation is the feather. Because production was very limited in wartime this is a rare variation.

© ROYAL DOULTON TABLEWARE LIMITED 1983
D.6710

THE CELEBRITY COLLECTION

by Royal Doulton
A hand-made, hand-decorated series

GROUCHO MARX
"I've worked myself up
from nothing to a state
of extreme poverty."

W.C. FIELDS
Designed by David Biggs
D6674   Large   1983-1986

Printed on the base, the special *Celebrity Collection* back stamp in suitable 'Odeon' style type. A facsimile signature of the artist and the quip *"I was in love with a beautiful blonde once. She drove me to drink 'tis the one thing I'm indebted to her for"*. See – American Express.

William Claude Fields (1879-1946) was unique as a comedian, actor, and raconteur. He was born in Philadelphia of English parents and began his career in vaudeville and on the English music halls. In Hollywood he appeared first in silent films, and then in movies until his death. The character he played was essentially the same in all his pictures, an inimitable figure. His most famous portrayal was of a flamboyant Mr. Micawber in *David Copperfield* (1935). He appeared opposite Mae West in *My Little Chicadee* (1940).

It's a funny old world – a man's lucky if he gets out of it alive.

MAE WEST
Designed by Colin M. Davidson
D6688   Large   1983-1986

Printed on the base, the special *Celebrity Collection* backstamp with a facsimile signature, and the quote: *When I'm good, I'm very good. But when I'm bad, I'm better.*

19

First issued in 1983 as a promotional item for American Express with an added backstamp 'Premier Edition for American Express'. Less than 500 marked in this way. See American Express.

Mae West (1892-1980) made her screen debut in 1932. She portrayed a glamourous, sophisticated character who loved luxury, men and a good time, and with no pretensions of wishing to reform. The picture's end found her wealthy, wicked and well loved. Her success was phenomenal, the public were delighted with her honesty, if Hay's Code administrators were not. She is renowned for her smart sayings.

It's not the men in my life, but the life in my men that counts.

LOUIS ARMSTRONG

Designed by David Biggs
D6706   Large   1984-1988

Printed on the base, the special *Celebrity Collection* backstamp with a facsimile signature and Satchmo's reply to the question, *'What is jazz?' Man if you gotta ask, you'll never know.*

Louis Armstrong (1900-1971) familiarly known as 'Satchel-Mouth' or 'Satchmo', was born in New Orleans. He was celebrated for his trumpet style of jazz. His technique was regarded as unique. It was said of him. "He occupies a place in hot music equated to that of Einstein in physics". With his band, he travelled the world and was loved by all. His gravelly vocal renderings of 'Hello Dolly' and 'What a Wonderful World' make one feel that it is indeed a wonderful world. Louis Armstrong and his wife were granted an audience with the Pope whilst on a visit to Rome. The Pope asked *'Have you any children?'* Satchmo replied, *'No sir, but we are having an awful lot of fun trying".* The Pope began to chuckle but was led away by an over-zealous cardinal.

GROUCHO MARX
Designed by Stan Taylor
D6710   Large   1984-1988

Printed on the base, the special *Celebrity Collection* back stamp with a facsimile signature and the quip. *I've worked myself up from nothing to a state of extreme poverty.* Groucho Marx (1895-1977) was the most dominant member of the Marx Brothers. He was renowned for his cutting quips levelled against women, money and himself.

Remember, men, we're fighting for the woman's honour; which is probably more than she ever did.

Any man who says he can see through a woman is missing a lot.

JIMMY DURANTE
Designed by David Biggs
D6708   Large   1985

Printed on the base, the special *Celebrity Collection* backstamp with a facsimile signature the quote: *Goodnight Mrs. Calabash, wherever you are.* A reference to his late wife Jeannne, whose early death he felt had been exacerbated by his success.

Jimmy Durante (1883-1979). Born in New York, he achieved fame as a cabaret artist. He played and sang to the piano in his own inimitable drawl, ballads such as 'The Day I found the Lost Chord'.

He made many records before trying his luck in Hollywood in 1931. He was an instant success and made many more films over the next thirty years. Much of his humour was directed at his own nose, a large feature that gave him his nickname 'The Schnozzola'.

Phil Silvers: *It's right under your nose*
Jimmy: *Don't be so indefinite.*
You're in the Army Now, 1941.

CLARK GABLE

Designed by Stan Taylor
D6709   Large   1984

Issued in the U.S.A., but recalled because of copyright difficulties.
Over 500 jugs escaped before recall.
Copyright approval is difficult to negotiate in North America where the person and later executors have the right to approve likeness.

Clark Gable (1901-1960). From early occupations as lumberjack, general handyman, theatre scene shifter and film extra, Clark Gable progressed to become 'The King' and one of the Movie greats.

In thirty years as leading man, he appeared with Hollywoods greatest stars, from Greta Garbo and Jean Harlow to Ava Gardener and Marilyn Monroe. He appeared in 1934 with Claudette Colbert in the witty romantic comedy *It Happened one Night* which won five Academy Awards. The following year he appeared with Charles Laughton in *Mutiny on the Bounty* and in 1939 was chosen for the coveted role of Rhett Butler in *Gone with the Wind*. His last film was *The Misfits* made shortly before his death.

He was a star with great charm and sex appeal, laced with a generous sense of humour. The representation of his ears apparently caused the jug to be rejected twice by his executors. I think I would have rejected it on the grounds that his habitual cheerful grin and handsome good looks were not portrayed.

Talent is the least important thing a performer needs, but humility is the one thing he must have.

ELVIS PRESLEY

Elvis Presley (1935-1977). The Rock and Roll idol of the '60s teenagers who has, after his untimely death, become a cult figure. He cut his first record for R.C.A. in 1956. Within one month 'Heartbreak Hotel' had rocketed to No.1 in all the charts, stayed there for eight weeks and sold three million copies.

'Elvis's style was impossible to define being an exciting mixture of country, gospel, rhythm and blues, pop, sex, rage, independence and arrogance. Spasms rocked his body as if it had been plugged into the same electrical source as his guitar.'
Tony Palmer.

I hope I haven't bored you.
Concluding his last Press Conference 1977.

U.K. Internatonal Ceramics have plans to issue this title in 1995.

MARILYN MONROE (1926-1962)

A star with many and undefinable charms. She was illegitimate and had a deprived childhood. She had an elfin innocent beauty and talent but was supremely unconfident. She loved and was loved by men. Her third husband, writer Arthur Miller created one of her most successful roles, opposite Clark Gable in *The Misfits* in 1961. Amongst her other memorable performances were those in *The Seven Year Itch* 1955 and *Some Like it Hot* 1959. She never found the security she sought and her death was early and tragic. She was mourned by the world who had taken her to their hearts, unfortunately something she never comprehended.

A sex symbol becomes a thing, I hate being a thing.

HUMPHREY BOGART (1899-1957)

Born into a wealthy New York family we went on to the stage in 1920 and later into films. They tough gangster personality he played in *The Petrified Forest* in 1936 stuck with him for thirty pictures. He emerged in the forties with his unconventional looks and sardonic style as the epitome of the 'tough loner, the disillusioned anti-hero, honest in a dishonest world'. All his performances were accomplished but *Casablanca* 1942 with Ingrid Berman; *To Have or Have Not* 1945 with Lauren Bacall (who became his fourth wife) and *African Queen* 1951 with Katharine Hepburn are memorable.

Here's looking at you kid.
                Casablanca.

Four celebrities were left out of the collection, mainly due to copyright difficulties: Elvis Presley, Marilyn Monroe, Humphrey Bogart and Clark Gable. The first three exist only as prototypes.

CHARACTER AND TOBY JUG COLLECTORS SOCIETY OF AUSTRALIA
see John Shorter and Clubs.

CHARACTER JUG OF THE YEAR

1991	D6874	FORTUNE TELLER
1992	D6907	WINSTON CHURCHILL
1993	D6907	VICE ADMIRAL LORD NELSON
1994	D6947	CAPT. HOOK
1995	D	CAPTAIN BLIGH

All large jugs with a production life of one year only.

CHARLIE CHAPLIN

Designed by Bill Harper
D6949   Large   1993

Commissioned by Lawleys by Post in a limited edition of 5,000.

In the character of 'The Little Tramp' with a cane handle.
©1989. Bubbles Inc.

Charles Chaplin (1889-1977) was born in London of theatrical parents. After an impoverished youth, he went to America with Fred Karno's troupe. Later he was invited to act in comedies for the Keystone Company. He based his walk on an old Londoner he knew, and created the character of the lovable little man with the baggy pants and oversized shoes. He went on to form his own production company and became the biggest box office draw of all time. He was the greatest star of the silent screen, and carried on his career into the 'talkies'.

His films always sought to speak the truth, not the accepted truth. They were comedies with a social message, attacking the evils of poverty, war, capitalism and bigotry. They include *The Gold Rush 1925, City Lights 1931 and Modern Times* in 1936, which was the last silent feature film produced. *Monsieur Verdoux*, in 1947, shocked the American middle class, for they were reminded of scandals in his personal life and his supposed left-wing leanings, so that when he sailed for England for the premiere of his film *Limelight* in 1952, the State Department, forgetting his contribution to the world supremacy of the American film industry, barred his return. He settled in Switzerland with his fourth wife Oona O'Neill, and died there, but not before he was forgiven and recalled to the U.S.A. where he was given a rapturous welcome; he was knighted by Queen Elizabeth in 1975.

Comedy is life viewed from a distance; tragedy life in a close-up.

All I need to make a comedy is a park, a policeman and a pretty girl.

KING CHARLES I

Designed by Bill Harper
D6917   Large   1992

Second in the *Fit for a King* series.
The first three handled Tyg. It commemorates the 350th anniversary of the start of the English Civil War.
A Limited Edition of 2,500. Special backstamp and certificate.
The handles represent his Queen Henrietta Maria, his opponent Oliver Cromwell and a hat plume.

Charles I (1625-1649) became king at 24 and reigned for 24 years. He was a high minded, cultivated gentleman but had strong prejudices and poor judgment. His marriage to Henrietta Maria, the Catholic daughter of the King of France was unpopular. The king was dogmatic and inflexible with his Parliament and attempted to usurp their power and govern by personal rule. Parliament raised its own army against the Royalists and there was Civil War for six years. Eventually defeated, Charles fled to Scotland but the Scottish handed him over to the Parliamentarians and he died bravely on the scaffold in Whitehall. Scotland thus escaped in the words of a popular Victorian song '*Being Knocked about a Bit*' by Cromwell when castles were blown up, so that they were no longer a threat and ecclesiastical buildings were denuded of their decoration and *Popery*. England Has forgiven but Ireland, which also declared for the King, never has.

A companion jug enters the range as we go to press:

OLIVER CROMWELL

Designed by Bill Harper
D6968   Large   1994

Two handled, one represents General Fairfax, Commander-in-Chief of the Parliamentary army in the civil war, and the other Charles I, who was defeated at the Battle of Naseby by the New Model Army formed by Cromwell and Fairfax.

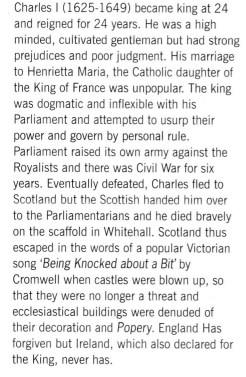

THE CHELSEA PENSIONER

Designed by Stan Taylor

D6817   Large   1991

Charles II (1660-1685) son of the above founded the Royal Hospital at Chelsea in 1682 as a retirement home for 400 soldiers. Here an inmate is seen in his brilliant summer uniform and his campaign medals are shown on the handle of the jug.

In 1988 this jug was released in the same colourway but with special backstamps for four U.S. Stores in a limited edition of 250 pieces each.

D6830   *Horne* 1st anniversary of Opening of Royal Doulton Room.
D6831   *Holmes* 1st anniversary
D6832   *Higbee* 3rd anniversary
D6833   *Strawbridge & Clothier* 2nd anniversary

You ask, 'What is our aim?' I can answer in one word: 'Victory!' Victory at all costs, victory in spite of all terror, victory however long and hard the road may be: for without victory there is no survival.

First speech as Prime Minister in the House of Commons, 13th May 1940.

CHURCHILL

Designed by Charles Noke

D6170   Large   1940-1941

Printed on the base: *Winston Spencer Churchill, Prime Minister of Britain, 1940. This loving cup was made during the Battle of Britain as a tribute to a great leader.*

This is a two-handled loving cup, as opposed to the usual jugs. The plain ivory finish gives a good sculptural quality to this very rare model.

Prototypes exist with added colour, different features and no quotation on the base.

Winston Spencer Churchill (1874-1965), the son of a beautiful American mother and an English aristocrat, had a long eventful life. He entered politics in 1900. He was Prime Minister on three occasions, notably in 1940 when he became Britain's war-time leader of a coalition government. He was a great orator and his war-time speeches were an inspiration to the free world. The British bulldog figure produced by Doulton is said to represent him and his dogged stubbornness never to accept defeat.

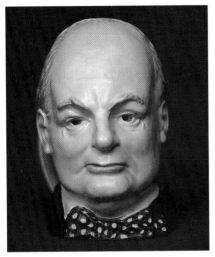

WINSTON CHURCHILL
SECOND VERSION

Designed by Stan Taylor
D6907   Large   1992

Character Jug of the Year.

Handle shows the Union Jack and the British bulldog. Churchill is portrayed as Prime Minister during the Second World War.

More than 30,000 of this popular jug were sold.

WINSTON CHURCHILL
THIRD VERSION

Designed by Stan Taylor
D6934   Small   1993-

Again the distinctive bow tie and cigar. The handle consists of a reproduction of the *News Chronicle of May* 8th 1945 which announces *"Today is V Day"* – this refers to victory in Europe.

27

THE CITY GENT

Designed by Stan Taylor
D6815   Large   1988-1991

There are not many bowler hats and rolled umbrellas in *The City* today. The international computer age has arrived and the last Dickensian office disappeared with the *Big Bang. The Square Mile*, the financial and commercial centre of the U.K. is now populated daily by 500,000 businessmen and women in fashionable suits.

This jug is included in *The London Collection.*

SANTA CLAUS

Designed by Michael Abberley
Peg Doll handle
D6668   Large   1981
Reindeer handle
D6675   Large   1982
Santa's Sack of Toys handle
D6690   Large   1983
Plain handle
D6704   Large   1984-
D6705   Small   1984-
D6706   Mini   1984-1991
D6950   Tiny   1993
D6940   Small Toby   1993

In 1981, '82 and '83 Royal Doulton introduced the Santa Claus jug with three different handles in the three successive years. This was a new departure for Doulton, making definite annual variations, probably a feature of great interest to collectors. In 1984 the Santa Claus jug appeared with a plain handle, and continues in production. Tiny remodelled by Bill Harper in a limited edition of 2,500 for *Seaway China Co.*; 102 Broadway, Marine City, MI 48039, U.S.A.
* Note the variations of modelling in the different sizes.

Santa Claus is a contraction of Saint Nicholas, the patron saint of children. The legend perpetuated by parents and toy manufacturers tells how Santa leaves his home at the North Pole on Christmas Eve and travels around the world. He rides in a sleigh drawn by reindeer, and piled high with presents. Landing on the roofs of houses, he climbs down chimneys and fills the waiting stockings of good boys and girls.

SANTA CLAUS
WITH HOLLY WREATH

Designed by Michael Abberley
D6794   Large   1988
Commissioned by Home Shopping Network (North
American T.V. Network) Florida, U.S.A. In a limited
edition of 5,000.
Sold out in three days.

D6900   Mini   1991-1992
A limited edition of 5,000
For sale in selected store outlets in U.S.

SANTA CLAUS
WITH CANDY CANE

Designed by Michael Abberley
D6793   Large   1988
Commissioned by Cable Value Network
(North American T.V. Network) U.S.A.

Remodelled by Bill Harper as
D6980   Tiny   1994
For *Seaway China*, U.S.A.
Limited Edition of 2,500. Special backstamp

SANTA CLAUS
WITH CANDY CANE

Variation with red, white and green stripes.
D6840   Large   1989

Commissioned by *American Collectors Society*
in a limited edition of 1,000.
Special Backstamp.

MRS. CLAUS

D6922   Mini   1992

Handle to left so that she can be paired with Santa Claus –
Holly Wreath miniature.
Available as all above in North American market only which
can be very frustrating for world-wide collectors.

THE CLOWN

Designed by Harry Fenton
D5610   Large Red haired
       1937-1942
D5610   Large Brown haired
       c.1937-42
D6322   Large White haired
       1951-1955

The two pre-war versions of this jug have the clown's more traditional face made up in white. One has a red, yellow and green ribbon in his 'desert orange' hair with a beribonned handle in the same colours. The other has hair and handle in shades of brown only. These jugs, whose production was curtailed by the Second World War, have the same registration number, so that it is not possible yet to ascertain which came first. Perhaps the paler is the 'watered-down', wartime version, as Doulton suggest it was made until 1942. This would give them a production life of about the same length, which is substantiated by the numbers of each which appear. The paler one being the rarer. The white-haired version is also rare, with only a five-year production span, and all three versions are very desirable additions to a collection.

The clown has entertained us for centuries with his juggling and acrobatics and, as a master of mime, has shown us the laughter and pathos of life. He has evolved through the years, aided by masters of his craft like Joseph Grimaldi, who gave him his affectionate nickname 'Joey'.

CLOWN
SECOND VERSION

Designed by Stan Taylor
D6834   Large   1989 -

Issued as a set of four *Circus Performers*. This is a much jollier Clown than the previous.

CLOWN

D6935   Small Toby   1993-

UNCLE TOM COBBLEIGH

Designed by Max Henk
D6337   Large   1952-1960

Old Uncle Tom Cobbleigh is a character in a traditional ballad 'Widdecombe Fair'. He and eight mates rode Tom Pearce's grey mare to the fair. Not surprisingly, the mare took sick and died, and is still to be seen with her ghostly crew haunting the moor at night. One of the mare's shoes forms the handle of this jug, made only in the large size.

When the wind whistles cold on moor of a night, Tom Pearce's old mare doth appear ghostly white.

UNCLE TOM COBBLEIGH-PROTOTYPE

Designed by Robert Tablenor in 1975. Not as successful a design as the 1952 version and never put into production.

COLEMANS
SPECIAL COMMISSION

Origin of this firm not known.

Large size character jugs and tobacco jar found overprinted.

FARMER JOHN   1938
JOHN BARLEYCORN   1939
PADDY TOBACCO JAR
There may be others.

Farmer John".

R♯N♡820500
REG♡IN AUSTRALIA

Coleman's Compliments

THE COLLECTING WORLD – SEE KEVIN FRANCIS.

CHRISTOPHER COLUMBUS

Designed by Stan Taylor
D6891   Large   1991

To commemorate the 500th anniversary of the discovery of the New World.

CHRISTOPHER COLUMBUS (1451-1506)

A Genoese explorer who, sponsored by Ferdinand and Isabella of Spain, and believing the world to be round set out to discover a sea route westwards to eastern Asia. Instead he made a landfall in the Bahamas. In three further voyages he explored from Cuba and Jamaica to Puerto Rico and Honduras and to the Orinoco on the mainland. All the while he believed his discoveries were in the Orient. Thus he is credited with the discovery of the Americas and consequently why native Americans North and South are labelled with the misnomer *'Indians'*.

CHRISTOPHER COLUMBUS

Designed by Stan Taylor
D6911   Small   1992

Commissioned by R.D.I.C.C. to commemorate the 500th anniversary of the discovery of the New World.
The *'Discovery'* edition is of 7,000.
Exhibited in the British Pavillion at Expo '92 Seville, Spain. Special backstamp and certificate and individually numbered.

Based on the previous jug but the chart of the original is replaced by Columbus's flagship, *Santa Maria* and his fur collar is now beige not black.

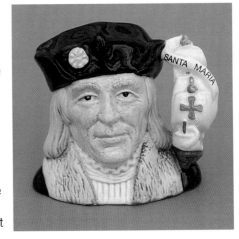

'COMRADES IN ARMS' SERIES

A set of three jugs designed by Bill Harper.

SAILOR	D6875	Small	1991-
SOLDIER	D6876	Small	1991-
AIRMAN	D6870	Small	1991-

This series pays tribute to the men who served in the armed forces in the Second World War, mainly conscripted men at that time.

The Navy is known as the *Senior Service* as it was formed under Henry VIII (1509-1547). This Naval Officer wears the informal dufflecoat and polo jumper needed for convoy duty during the War when the Navy's main task was to keep the shipping lines open for vital supplies to reach the U.K. The handle is formed of a pair of binoculars used to keep a good watch for enemy U-Boats.

The Army was raised in Charles II's reign (1600-1685). This Soldier wears a netted *Tin Hat,* a *Balaclava* and the shoulder flash

of *The Desert Rats* as worn by Soldiers of the 8th Army who fought in the North African campaign. The *rat* was a jerboa, capable of great leaps forward. The handle is formed by a bayonet and a water canteen.

The Royal Air Force formed in 1918 played a very important role in 1940 in defeating the German Luftwaffe over southern England in *The Battle of Britain.*

A member of the Doulton family, Flying Officer Michael Duke Doulton, who at 6' 8" was the tallest flyer in the R.A.F. was shot down and killed at this time. The present Michael Doulton was named after him.

The handle shows a German plane shot down in flames.

No mention here of the womens services but another set was commissioned to represent the Canadian Armed Forces who fought side by side with their British compatriots.

"ON GUARD FOR THEE"

CANADIAN	SAILOR	D6704	Small 1991	– Dark brown coat. R.C.N. on binoculars.
CANADIAN	SOLDIER	D6905	Small 1991	– Red patch on canteen.
CANADIAN	AIRMAN	D6903	Small 1991	– Red scarf has cypher R.C.A.F.

Commissioned by *The British Toby,* Toronto to mark the International Collectors Weekend September 1991 in a limited edition of 250 sets.

The title is taken from the Canadian National Anthem.

Never in the field of human conflict was so much owed by so many to so few. W.S. Churchill.

THE COOK AND THE CHESHIRE CAT

Designed by Bill Harper

D6842   Large   1990-1991

Based on the drawings of Sir John Tenniel The Cook and Cheshire Cat are characters in *Alice's Adventures in Wonderland* by Lewis Carroll. They belonged in the Duchess's household and both were a law unto themselves. When the Cook was not showering pepper into her pot and over the kitchen, she was throwing the saucepans, plates and dishes, and anything to hand, at the Duchess, Alice and the baby. The cat grinned because he was *a Cheshire Cat* the Duchess explained to Alice. It had a habit of disappearing leaving only its grin. When it upset the Queen of Hearts and she ordered its execution, a dispute arose as its body had disappeared and the executioner said it was impossible to cut off a head if there was no body!

'Well, I've often seen a cat without a grin" thought Alice, *"but a grin without a cat! It's the most curious thing I ever saw in my life".*

ROBINSON CRUSOE

Designed by Max Henk

D6532	Large	1960-1983
D6539	Small	1960-1983
D6546	Mini	1960-1983

In 1704 Alexander Selkirk was marooned on an uninhabited island for five years. Daniel Defoe based a novel on these experiences, successfully embroidering them with added incidents, so that the book, first published in 1719, has been read ever since. Now usually abridged as a children's adventure story, it appears as a pantomime at Christmas. Here Man Friday peeps around the palm tree handle.

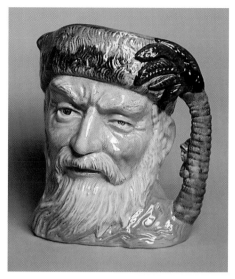

His favourite saying:
When found make a note of it.

CAP'N CUTTLE

Designed by Charles Noke with later models by Harry Fenton

D5842	Mid Size	1938-1945
D5842	Small	1948-1960
D6266	Small Toby Jug	1948-1960
D5842	Table Lighter	1958

Captain Edward Cuttle from *Dombey & Son* (1846) by Charles Dickens. *A gentlemen in a wide suit of blue, with a hook instead of a hand attached to his right wrist; very bushy black eyebrows; and a thick stick in his left hand covered all over (like his nose) with knobs. He wore a loose black silk handkerchief round his neck and such a very large coarse shirt collar, that it looked like a small sail.*

DARLEY & SON

(Department Stores)

Sheffield and Rotherham.

Small size character jugs overprinted *Souvenir from Darley & Son, Sheffield and Rotherham. Tony Weller, Jester, Parson Brown* and *Sairey Gamp* have been found. There may be others.

THE DIAMOND COLLECTION

To commemorate the Diamond Jubilee of Doulton Character jugs 1994. Six early subjects by Charles Noke and Harry Fenton remodelled by Bill Harper, who says, he quite likes the precision and exactness required in working on tinies.

D6951	DICK TURPIN
D6954	GRANNY
D6952	JOHN BARLEYCORN
D6955	PARSON BROWN
D6953	JESTER
D6956	SIMON THE CELLARER

Limited edition of 2,500 Individually numbered and certificate. Special diamond-shaped display stand.The certificate is included within a brochure in the style of the first one for character jugs, published in 1935.

Previously known as *face jugs* the title *character jug* was first used in 1935.

CHARLES DICKENS

Designed by   D   Large   1995
Two handled, each handle with three of his characters. To commemorate the 125th anniversary of his death. Limited edition of 2,500.

CHARLES DICKENS

Designed by Bill Harper
D6901 Small   1991

Commissioned by R.D.I.C.C.
Limited edition of 7,500
Individually numbered and certificate.
Handle consists of an inkwell based on one in the Dickens House Museum, Doughty St. London
Standing on a copy of *The Old Curiosity Shop*, written 150 years ago in 1891.

The special backstamp includes a quotation from G.K. Chesterton *'Whatever the word 'great' means, Dickens was what it means.'*

Charles Dickens (1812-1970), Englands great popular novelist of the nineteenth century. He had little formal education and when his father was imprisoned for debt in Marshalsea Prison during 1824, the young Charles spent five months in Johnathan Warren's blacking factory on the Thames at Charing Cross sticking labels on early Doulton and Watts pots. As did his hero of *David Copperfield* (1850) which is largely biographical. Dickens visited the Doulton Lambeth factory many years later as a famous author, on seeing the stoneware jars he is reported as saying *"When I was a boy at Warren's Blacking Warehouse, I filled many thousand of those!"* The Royal Doulton Magazine December 1953 – See also *Doulton Lambeth Adverting Wares* Page 157.

Dickens novels were favourite reading with Charles Noke who created the character jug range so that it is not surprising that the characters from Dickens novels appear so often among them. Noke himself is credited with the early designs of *Buz Fuz, Captain Cuttle, Fat Boy, Sairey Gamp, Mr. Micawber, Mr. Pickwick* and *Tony and Sam Weller*.

THE DICKENS TINIES

About 1.5in (3 cm) high, these Tinies were issued to celebrate the 170th Anniversary of Dickens' Birth. 1982-

		Designed by
D6677	OLIVER TWIST from *Oliver Twist*	Robert Tabbenor
D6678	ARTFUL DODGER from *Oliver Twist*	Peter Gee
D6679	FAGIN from *Oliver Twist*	Robert Tabbenor
D6680	DAVID COPPERFIELD from *David Copperfield*	M. Abberley
D6681	LITTLE NELL from *The Old Curiosity Shop*	M. Abberley
D6682	URIAH HEEP from *David Copperfield*	Robert Tabbenor
D6683	SCROOGE from *A Christmas Carol*	M. Abberley
D6684	BILL SYKES from *Oliver Twist*	M. Abberley
D6685	BETSY TROTWOOD from *David Copperfield*	M. Abberley
D6686	MR. BUMBLE from *Oliver Twist*	Robert Tabbenor
D6687	MRS. BARDELL from *Pickwick Papers*	Robert Tabbenor
D6688	CHARLES DICKENS	Eric Griffiths

Complete with a certificate and leaflet giving details of each character, also a mahogany display shelf. Issued 1982-1984 in the U.K. and available only via Lawley's Mail Order Service, they became available in the U.S.A., Canada and Australia later.

OLIVER TWIST (D6677) is an orphan who escapes from MR. BUMBLE (D6686), beadle of the parish workhouse where he was born, and runs away to London. There he is discovered by the ARTFUL DODGER (D6678) who enlists him in the gang of boys who steal for FAGIN (D6679). A receiver and leader of the gang, it is Fagin who tells BILL SYKES (D6684) of Nancy's intention to free Oliver from their clutches so that Sikes, a brutal thief, murders her. Doulton always spell Sikes with a 'y', Dickens spelt it with an 'i'.

DAVID COPPERFIELD (D6680) is also an orphan, but he has a great aunt, BETSY TROTWOOD (D6685), with a kind heart under a forbidding exterior, who takes care of him. URIAH HEEP (D6682), a hypocritical clerk, is the villain of *David Copperfield*. MRS. BARDELL (D6687) sues Mr. Pickwick for breach of promise in *The Pickwick Papers*. SCROOGE (D6683) is a miser, who is reformed when he is visited by ghosts on Christmas Eve, in *A Christmas Carol*.

LITTLE NELL (D6681) is the central figure of *The Old Curiosity Shop,* and her death reduced her creator to tears when he wrote that episode.

The creator of these brilliantly drawn characters, and many more, was CHARLES DICKENS (D6688), who completes this set of subjects.

DILLARDS, New Orleans, Louisiana, U.S.A.

A department store with a Royal Doulton room.
D6883 YEOMAN OF THE GUARD Large 1990. 50 copies only with special backstamp.

THE DOULTON FAMILY

JOHN DOULTON

Designed by Eric Griffiths
D6656   Small   1980-

Printed on the base is the special backstamp of the Royal Doulton International Collectors' Club, formed in 1980.
John Doulton 1793-1873.
Exclusively for Collectors' Club.

This jug was the first of the special Club issues and can be purchased by each new member. Big Ben's clock face during the first year of issue showed a time of 8 o'clock and thereafter 2 o'clock.
Founder members therefore have the rarer model.

John Doulton (1793-1873) was born at Fulham in London and served an apprenticeship at the local pottery. In 1812 he had the opportunity to join a small pottery on the South Bank of the Thames, and in three years he had become part proprietor with John Watts. He was always hard working and acquired the reputation of being one of the most practical potters in London. Most of the products at this time were strictly utilitarian. The firm of Doulton and Watts moved to Lambeth and expanded rapidly, acquiring less successful neighbours. When he died at 1873, aged 80, John Doulton left a large, thriving business in the capable hands of his son Henry. The pottery remained at Lambeth until 1956.

'Are you working, boy?'
'Yes, sir.'
'Well I don't see any sweat on your nose.'

D.6656

JOHN DOULTON
1793 - 1873
EXCLUSIVELY FOR
COLLECTORS CLUB
© ROYAL DOULTON
TABLEWARE LTD 1980

SIR HENRY DOULTON

Designed by Eric Griffiths, modelled by Bill Harper
D6703   Small 4.5 in.   1984

Printed on the base is the special backstamp of the R.D.I.C.C. and *Sir Henry Doulton 1820-1897. Exclusively for Collectors' Club.* Also a facsimile signature of the designer Eric Griffiths.

Henry Doulton (1820-1897) was the second son of John Doulton, and he entered the firm at the age of 15. Although artistic and sensitive by nature, he also had a certain dynamism and aptitude for business. Quite late in life, after accumulating a large fortune from the sale of the pottery's utilitarian products, he was persuaded to create a department to produce art works. The success of its first productions fired his enthusiasm. With great foresight, he gave his artists, mainly ex-students of The Lambeth School of Art – many of them women – freedom to develop their own styles. In return, their work won him many prizes at major exhibitions and many other honours, including a knighthood.

In the 1880s he gained a second factory at Burslem, Staffordshire, in the heart of the English 'Potteries'. He said of the local opposition, *In their view we Southerners know little about God and nothing at all about potting.* His business acumen was such that, whilst few of his competitors remain, the Burslem factory flourishes to this day.

There are three things that go to make a success of a firm. First quality of output, secondly prompt execution of orders and thirdly price, and always in that order. You can get a good price for a fine thing more easily than you can get a poor price for a bad thing. Besides, the one does you good, the other does you a lot of harm.

ROYAL DOULTON PROMOTIONAL ISSUES
MICHAEL DOULTON

Designed by Bill Harper
D6808   Small   1988-1989

Honorary President of the R.D.I.C.C., Michael Doulton is the great, great, grandson of John Doulton. He travels the world representing Royal Doulton and promoting the products.

These jugs can only be purchased at promotional events attended by Michael Doulton. It bears his signature. During 1978-1982 an adaption of *John Barleycorn* was offered in the same way.

MICHAEL AND SIR HENRY DOULTON

Designed by Bill Harper
D6921   Small   1992-1993

A double-sided jug, a rarity in the small size. The Doulton logo is reversed on the forward side.

DRAKE

Designed by Harry Fenton
D6115   Large   c.1940-1960
D6174   Small   1941-1960

Sir Francis Drake (c.1545-1596) was a figure of dash and daring in English history. He was the first Englishman to circumnavigate the world, and played a large part in wresting control of the seas from Spain. He buccaneered his way amongst the great Spanish fleets, to a glorious and final victory against the Spanish Armada sent to invade England in 1588.

'*HATLESS*' DRAKE is a rare early variation. It is not a Pilot as they were retailed in 1940 and usually bear that date (+13). D6115.

There is an even rarer green version. On the reverse is embossed *Drake he was a Devon Man*. On the base *Drake. Hatless* is a popular label. It seems probable that this jug was sold only during 1940 and the version with hat introduced late 1940 or 1941.

SIR FRANCIS DRAKE

Designed by Peter Gee
D6805   Large   1988

Special numbered edition of 6,000. A Guild
exclusive to celebrate the 400th anniversary of
the defeat of the Spanish Armada. These jugs
were presented as prizes at a game of bowls
played on Plymouth Hoe in 1988, 400 years
after the game which Drake and his captains
played after the sighting of the Spanish
Armada in the English Channel.

According to legend Drake finished his game in
a leisurely fashion before sailing to harass the
superior Spanish fleet. The leisurely start was
in fact due to the practical reason of waiting for the tide.

If the Dons sight Devon, I'll quit the port of heaven, an'drum them up the Channel as we
drummed them long ago.
Drakes Drum – Newbolt.

KING EDWARD VII

Designed by Bill Harper
D6923   Small   1992

A lavishly decorated and gilded jug.

Commissioned by the R.D.I.C.C in a limited
edition of 2,500. Numbered.

The handle has the Lion and Crown of the
Doulton logo. To represent the Royal Warrant
awarded to the company in 1902 soon after
his accession. The idea for this title originated
with an R.D.I.C.C member.

Edward VII (1901-1910) was almost 60 and
a grandfather when he succeeded and his
mother had previously denied him his royal duties. Consequently he had gained the
reputation as a playboy. However in his short reign he proved an able King with a *forte* for
foreign affairs. He showed great diplomacy and forged many useful links abroad and was
dubbed *Edward the Peacemaker*. He showed the tact, warmth and consideration for others
his mother never did and he was popular with his subjects.

He had succeeded in his Kingly profession and he had the instinct of peace
W.S. Blunt

ELEPHANT TRAINER

Designed by Stan Taylor

D6841 Large 1990-1993

One of four *Circus Performers.*
Pre-released in the U.S.A. to four store outlets in 1989.
Limited editions of 250 each with special backstamps.
Higbee Co. to celebrate 4th anniversary
Hornes, Holmes & Strawbridge & Clothier
'To commemorate the opening of their Royal Doulton Rooms in the United States of America'.

It is an amazing fact that an enormous elephant can be trained to obey the commands of his *mahout,* although he may be only a small boy. In India the elephants enormous strength has long been used in this way for heavy work. The *mahout* of this jug is Indian and very resplendent in his vermilion turban. A colourful member of the circus who trains the performing elephants.

THE ELF

Designed by Bill Harper
D6942 Mini 1993
D Small 1994

Available through U.S. outlets only.
An allocation available to *R.D.I.C.C.* members.

Fairy people were called elves in Scandinavia and were believed in long after the coming of Christianity. Being the resident fairies of Lapland is probably why they have become Santa's helpers.

E.P.C.O.T. CENTRE
Orlando, Florida, U.S.A.

BENJAMIN FRANKLIN
D6695 Small 1982
MARK TWAIN
D6694 Small 1982

These two jugs were exclusive to Walt Disney's last great project, The Experimental Prototype Community of Tomorrow during 1982 and entered the general range in 1983.

FALCONER
Designed by Max Henk
D6533　Large　1960-1992
D6540　Small　1960-1992
D6547　Mini　1960-1992

FALCONER
D6798　Large　1987
New colourway with a dark brown coat and
dark green hat commission by *Joseph Horne*
(Department store) Pittsburgh, U.S.A. in a
limited edition of 250. To celebrate the
opening of the Doulton room November 1987.

FALCONER
D6800　Large　1987
New colourway with maroon and cream striped hat. Limited edition of 1,000 commissioned
by *Peter Jones (China) Ltd.,* Yorks. U.K.

The falconer hunted with hawks and other birds of prey, training them to capture birds on
the wing and bring them back to their keeper. He wore a leather gauntlet and attached the
bird to his wrist, sometimes with a chain. The hawk would be hooded, but upon the hood
being removed would take flight. In earlier times it was a sport of kings and gentlemen. It
declined in England in the seventeenth century.

FALSTAFF
Designed by Harry Fenton
D6287	Large	1950-
D6385	Small	1950-
D6519	Mini	1960-92
D6062	Toby Jug-Large	1939-92
D6063	Toby Jug-Small	1939-92
D6385	Liqueur Flask	c.1960
D6385	Table Lighter	1958-1973

FALSTAFF
D6795 Large　　1987

Limited edition of 1,500 in new colourway
Commissioned by *U.K. Fairs Ltd.* to celebrate the fifth
annual Doulton Collectors Fair at the *Park Lane Hotel*
Piccadilly on 25th October 1987.

Sir John Falstaff appears in Shakespeare's *Henry IV* and *The Merry Wives of Windsor* – a fat, witty, good humoured old knight, loving jests, self-indulgent and over-addicted to sack. He appears as a friend and mentor of the spirited young Prince Hal in the historical drama *Henry IV, Part I,* but at the end of *Part II,* when the prince ascends the throne to become Henry V, he banishes his old friend from his presence.
The Merry Wives of Windsor is a comedy when happier days are recounted.

FAT BOY

Designed by Charles Noke with the later models by Harry Fenton

D5840	Mid Size	1938-1948
D5840	Small	1948-1960
D6139	Mini	1940-1960
D6142	Tiny	1940-1960
M59	Napkin Ring	c.1935-1939
D6264	Seated Toby	1948-1960

Fat Boy, Joe, was servant to Mr. Wardle in *The Pickwick Papers* (1837) by Charles Dickens.

The fat boy rose, opened his eyes, swallowed the huge piece of pie he had been in the act of masticating when he last fell asleep, and slowly obeyed his master's orders.

GUY FAWKES

Designed by Bill Harper
D6861   Large   1991

Pre-released by *Canadian Art and Collectables Show.* At their third Doulton show in Durham, Ontario May 1990. Limited edition of 750. Special backstamp. With the variation of an orange hat band.

Guy Fawkes (1570-1606) was one of a group of Catholic conspirators who planned the *Gunpowder Plot* to blow up King James I and both Houses of Parliament. On the fourth of November 1605 Guy Fawkes was arrested in the cellars of the House of Parliament. He and his fellow conspirators were tortured and executed. The event is commemorated in England every year on *Bonfire Night* when a *Guy* is burned on top of the bonfire with fireworks and general celebration.

Please to remember the fifth of November, gunpowder treason and plot;
we know no reason why gunpowder treason should ever be forgot.

1826 Broadsheet.

THE FIREMAN

Designed by Robert Tabbenor
D6697   Large   1984-1991

Commissioned by Griffith Pottery House, U.S.A.
Printed on the base: *Hand made and hand decorated. Designed by Jerry D. Griffith. Modelled by Robert Tabbenor.* Exclusive to Griffith Pottery House during 1983, but available generally in 1984, with modified backstamp. The hose nozzle varies in colour between deep orange and yellow.

Every small boy looks on the fireman's occupation as an enviable one – dashing through the streets with sirens sounding, fighting fires and making daring rescues. This fireman, from the United States, wears a characteristic large, leather helmet and corduroy-collared fire coat.

For *Fireman* D6839 Small see *Lawleys by Post.*

FOOTBALL SUPPORTER

Designed by Stan Taylor

D6927	ARSENAL	1992
D6931	ASTON VILLA	1992
D6925	CELTIC	1992
D6926	EVERTON	1992
D6930	LIVERPOOL	1992
D6928	LEEDS UNITED	1992
D6924	MANCHESTER UNITED	1992
D6929	RANGERS	1992

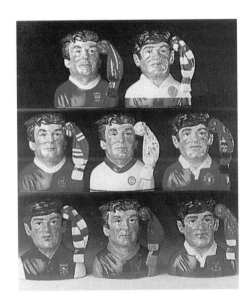

All small size. With two different models, seen in collar shapes, designed to be decorated with colours and crests of any football team. Jugs available from individual clubs. Obviously more clubs will commission jugs in the future.

SHEFFIELD WEDNESDAY

D6958   Small   1993

Commissioned by *John Sinclair* of Sheffield and available through them.

TERRY FOX

Designed by Bill Harper
D6881   Large   1990

Only three copies made to commemorate the Tenth anniversary of the *Marathon of Hope.*

No.1 presented to the Fox family.
No.2 auctioned by *Sotheby's* Canada for $32,000 at the *International Royal Doulton Collectors Weekend* September 15th 1990. Toronto, Canada.
Proceeds to the *Terry Fox Run.*
No.3 is in the *Sir Henry Doulton Gallery* Burslem.
Terry Fox (1958-1981) a young Canadian athlete who at 18 had lost a leg through bone cancer. He embarked on a *Marathon of Hope* across Canada to raise funds for cancer research. Unable to complete the run, because of lung cancer and his subsequent death, he inspired millions to run on an annual national event, *The Terry Fox Run.* This takes place on the anniversary of his death in June and raises millions of dollars for cancer research.

FORTUNE TELLER

Designed by Garry Sharpe
D6497   Large   1959-1967
D6503   Small   1959-1967
D6523   Mini   1960-1967

The Fortune Teller here is an 'gipsy' woman with large gold crescent earrings, indicative of her eastern origins. Her eyes gaze into the future. On the handle of the jug are the signs of the Zodiac which she affirms influence man's fate by predetermined patterns.

FORTUNE TELLER
SECOND VERSION

Designed by Stan Taylor
D6874   Large   1991

Handle includes Tarot cards.
Character Jug of the Year.

In a quaint caravan there's a lady they call the gipsy. She'll look in the future and drive away all your fears.
The Gipsy – popular song 1945

Bill Harper shows the model of the Terry Fox jug to Mrs Fox

BENJAMIN FRANKLIN

Designed by Eric Griffiths
D6695   Small   1983-1989

New style backstamp introduced in 1982
including the statement 'Hand made and hand
decorated';

Small size exclusive to Walt Disney's EPCOT
Center in Orlando, Florida U.S.A, during 1982.
(EPCOT = Experimental Prototype Community of
Tomorrow – Disney's last great project.)

Benjamin Franklin (1706-1790) was one of the
original revolutionary leaders who became a
valued member of the first Convention of American States. He had the shrewdness and
humour of the Yankee, was intelligent and had a good knowledge of his fellow men,
which made him a great diplomatist.
The kite and key of the handle refer to but one of his many talents, that of an amateur
scientist whose discoveries were very positive.

There never was a good war, or a bad peace. 1783.

SAIREY GAMP

Designed by Charles Noke with the later
models by Harry Fenton

D5451	Large	1935-1986
D5528	Small	1935-1986
D6045	Mini	1939-1986
D6146	Tiny	1940-1960
HN1625	Bookend	1936-c.1939
D6009	Ash Bowl	1939-1960
D6011	Sugar Bowl	1939-1942
D6015	Teapot	1939-1942
D6047	Bust	1939-1960
D6150	Toothpick Holder	1940-1942
M62	Napkin Ring	c.1935-1939
D6263	Small Toby Jug	1948-1960

See Special Commissions – *Strawbridge
and Clothier, Bentalls and Darley.*

Sairey Gamp – from *Martin Chuzzlewit* (1843) by Charles Dickens. A midwife and watcher
of the dying, Sarah Gamp, with her umbrella, bottle and imaginary colleague, Mrs. Harris,
is a source of some humour to the reader.

*She was a fat old woman, this Mrs. Gamp, with a husky voice and a moist eye... The face –
the nose in particular – was somewhat red and swollen, and it was difficult to enjoy her
society without becoming conscious of a smell of spirits.*

GARDENER

Designed by David Biggs

D6630	Large	1973-1981
D6634	Small	1973-1981
D6638	Mini	1973-1981

This must be the oldest profession, as
Adam was the first gardener.

Today our gardening experts are more
scientific than the cheerful character
portrayed on this jug. He is obviously one
of the old school. He will have been a
gardener all his life, man and boy, through
many seasons. With very little 'book-
learning', but a homely philosopher of life,
his experience and 'green fingers' will
make him king of all he surveys. The plants will flourish under his care and the friendly
robin always find a convenient perch on the handle of his spade.

GARDENER
SECOND VERSION
Designed by Stan Taylor
D6867   Large   1990-1991
D6868   Small   1990-1994

Pre-release at *National Garden Festival,*
Gateshead, U.K. May 1990. Unusually large
and small sizes are modelled quite differently,
two different characters but both seem rather
professional. Hired by customers to do the
back-breaking work while they sit back and
admire the results.

One is nearer God's heart in a garden
than anywhere else on earth.
                              Dorothy Gurney.

THE GENIE
Designed by Stan Taylor
D6892   Large   1991

The Genie is a sprite associated with Arabian
story telling. The Genie can be of either sex
and be good or evil. This is obviously the
Genie whom Aladdin released as he has the
old lamp in which he was imprisoned as a
handle. The flame of the lamp becomes the
Genie's pigtail in a clever design.

One of three *Mystical characters* including *The*
Witch and *The Wizard* introduced in 1990 and
1991. *The Genie* and *The Witch* had a
production of only one year.

ALADDIN'S GENIE
Designed by David Biggs
D6971   Large   1994

This is the first character jug to be produced
with a flambé glaze. Limited edition of 1500.
Walt Disney's 'Aladdin' was on general release
in 1994.

ST. GEORGE

Designed by Max Henk

D6618	Large	1968-1975
D6621	Small	1968-1975

Saint George has been England's patron saint since 1344. In former times St. George's Day, 23rd April, was celebrated in English towns and villages by pageants and processions in which the old legend was played out. A gallant St. George, armour glad and riding a noble charger, and a fearsome dragon with snapping jaws, were the principal performers. England's greatest writer, Shakespeare, was born and died on St. George's Day.

Cry God for Harry!
England and Saint George!

Henry V – Shakespeare

TOBY GILLETTE

Designed by Eric Griffiths

D6717   Large   1984

Only three copies made.

One was presented to Toby Gillette, an eleven-year-old schoolboy, by Jimmy Savile on his show, *Jim'll Fix It,* for BBC Television, transmitted on 10th March 1984. Toby asked Jim to 'fix' having a character jug made in his own likeness. Toby visited the Royal Doulton Factory and assisted in the various processes by which his jug was made. Another copy was auctioned at Sotheby's on 22nd May 1984 the proceeds to go to the Jimmy Savile Charitable Trust. The sale realised £15,950. A third copy remains in the Sir Henry Doulton Museum. Subsequently Toby sold his copy at Sotheby's in May 1986.

JOHN GILPIN
Designed by David Biggs
A large prototype.

Probably never put into production as the character is not well known outside the U.K. It has an airbrushed rim and the A. mark.

John Gilpin appears in a ballad by *William Cowper* (1731-1800). He was a city linen draper whose wife decided to celebrate their twentieth wedding anniversary with an outing to *The Bell* at Edmonton. He sent his wife, sister-in-law and the children ahead in the coach and borrowed a horse for himself, which he couldn't control. The horse galloped with him to Edmonton and ten miles beyond to Ware and returned with him to his stable without stopping The day was a complete disaster. The handle is a signpost, on one side is Edmonton the other Ware.

Away went Gilpin, neck or nought;
away went hat and wig; he little dreamt,
when he set out, of running such a rig.

William Cowper

GLADIATOR
Designed by Max Henk
D6550   Large   1961-1967
D6553   Small   1961-1967
D6556   Mini   1961-1967

The gladiator here wears the full armour of his profession, and the handle is formed by his shield and sword (*gladius* – Latin) which gives him his name. He was a champion, trained to display his skills in fighting for the amusement or the honour of the Roman Patrician who paid him. He provided much entertainment in the amphitheatre where he was matched against other fighters and wild beasts.

GLADSTONE POTTERY MUSEUM
(Working museum). Longton, Stoke-on-Trent.

The potteries grew up in North Staffordshire, because it was situated on top of one of Europe's richest coalfields and because of local skills in the use of clay.

With the passing of the Clean Air Act the practice of firing pottery ovens with coal ceased.
In 1978 Gladstone Pottery Museum organised the last firing of a bottle oven in Stoke-on-Trent. A full record on film was made of all the procedures. The oven was fired over one and a half days, the whole event taking one week. Royal Doulton character jugs were included and marked with the special backstamp used on the occasion. One of these, *Beefeater*, is exhibited by the Sir Henry Doulton Museum, Burslem. Another found is *Henry VIII,* there are others.

The backstamp states *Fired in the last firing of a traditional bottle oven 1978 Longton, Stoke-on-Trent, England.*

GLADSTONE POTTERY MUSEUM is open to the public each day (except Mondays, from October to May). It is close to the BESWICK factory and well worth a visit.

GOLFER
Designed by David Biggs
D6623   Large   1971-
D6756   Small   1987-
D6757   Mini   1987-1991

This jug is modelled in the likeness of Mr. W.J. Carey who was Chairman of the Doulton Company in the U.S.A. at the time. Golf is Scotland's national game and has been played there for over 500 years. This game 'in which small hard balls are struck with clubs having wooden or metal heads into a series of holes on smooth greens at varying distances apart and separated by fairways, rough ground, hazards, etc. the object to hole the ball in the fewest possible strokes', (*The Oxford English Dictionary)* has spread throughout the world and become one of the most popular pastimes.

If you watch a game, it's fun.
If you play it, it's recreation.
If you work at it, it's golf.
                                    Bob Hope.

GOLFER
New Colourway
D6787   Large   1987-
Limited edition of 1,000

Commissioned by *John Sinclair,*
Sheffield

GOLFER
SECOND VERSION
Designed by Stan Taylor
D6865   Small   1990-

Twenty years later we have a more
modern golfer. The game is as popular
as ever and truly international. Are the
Japanese buying up bits of Australia for
golf courses because they have run out
of room at home? This small jug was
issued with other sporting and
occupational jugs at this time.

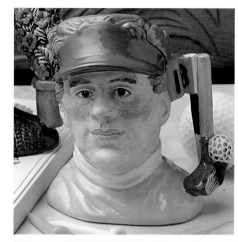

Golfer's Bowl
Burslem
D3394   8"   1911-1932

GONDOLIER
Designed by David Biggs
D6589   Large   1964-1969
D6592   Small   1964-1969
D6595   Mini   1964-1969

Our Gondolier is found in Venice poling
his shallow-draughted, high-prowed,
traditional craft through the canals and
lagoons. His dress of a striped jersey
and straw boater is traditional too, also
his ability to break into song. Motor
boats have threatened his livelihood,
but with visitors, especially lovers, he
will always be in demand, spending
little time moored to the striped
mooring post supporting this handle.

53

GONE AWAY

Designed by Garry Sharpe

D6531	Large	1960-1982
D6538	Small	1960-1982
D6546	Mini	1960-1982

Our huntsman here has a rather quizzical expression as if he is wondering how his quarry has eluded him. The fox at the handle, on the other hand, has an extremely knowing expression.

'Gone away!' – huntman's call when the quarry has been lost.

There was a jolly huntsman
in coat of scarlet red;
All day he hunted fast and free
as fox or vixen led;
Then 'Tally-Ho' rode home again,
to supper and to bed.

    The Huntsman by Walter de la Mare.

W.G. GRACE

Designed by Stan Taylor

D6845   Small   1989

Commissioned by *Lawleys by Post* in an Edition of 9,500

Special Backstamp. Numbered and certificate.

Dr. William G. Grace (1848-1915) *The Champion.* A country doctor by profession he played first class cricket for more than 50 years and influenced modern batting and bowling techniques more than any other. He was an imposing figure, over six feet tall with a full beard. He scored 55,000 runs and took nearly 2,900 wickets and remains a great cricket legend. He is seen in the cap of the *M.C.C. Marylebone Cricket Club.*

THE GRADUATE

Designed by Stan Taylor
D6916   Small   1991-

Handle formed as a degree certificate.

Doulton designate this jug *The Graduate (Male)* so they probably intend to produce *A Graduate (Female)*. Female faces don't interpret so well in a character jug but it is a shame more women are not acknowledged in this way. The title is issued to fill the need for gifts on the occasion of a Graduation.

The next jug shows that *'wrinklies'* make the best subjects with lots of character for the modeller to utilise.

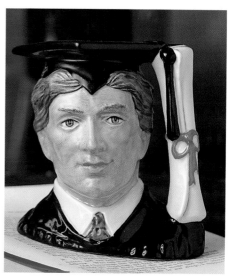

GRANNY

Designed by Harry Fenton and Max Henk

D5524	Large	1935-1983
D6384	Small	1953-1983
D6520	Mini	1960-1983
D6954	Tiny	1994

The small and miniature sizes were modelled by Max Henk and the Tiny by Bill Harper for the *Diamond Collection*.

TOOTHLESS GRANNY

The early version of the large size jug 1935-c. 1940 is modelled without a protruding tooth and with a plain handle. The later version has a coloured skein of wool as a handle. Small and large jugs often appear in the sale room with a fine dentistry job done on them! As the early jug is rarer and more valuable.

The granny of this jug belongs to an age gone by. Grannies don't look like this any more, they are much more modern today. However, they are still a great favourite with their grandchildren with whom they have time to play and to give a sympathetic ear when needed.

GRIFFITHS POTTERY HOUSE 100 Lorraine Avenue, Oreland, Pa 19075, U.S.A.
THE FIREMAN Designed by Robert Tabbenor D6697   Large   1983
Devised by Jerry Griffith and sold exclusively by the above company in 1983. During 1983
there were three variations to the backstamp. Included in the general range from 1984.

See *Fireman*

GUARDSMAN
Designed by Stan Taylor
D6755   Large   1986 -
D6771   Small   1987-1994
D6772   Mini   1987-1991

This Guardsman has the dress uniform of the
Grenadier guards, one of the regiments of the
Royal Household Division who guard the
royal palaces and attend at ceremonials
where they are a great tourist attraction. They
are, when not on ceremonial duties, serving
men of the British Army.

The handle is formed by a plain flag draped
over a bayonet. A Union Jack had been
proposed but was probably felt to demand
too complicated a finish.

GUILD OF SPECIALIST CHINA & GLASS RETAILERS, U.K.
An association of U.K. retailers who
have commissioned the following:

SCARAMOUCHE
Designed by Stan Taylor
D6774 Large   1987
Limited edition of 1,5000
Entered the general range in a different colourway.
1989-1991

SIR FRANCIS DRAKE
Designed by Peter Gee
D6805   Large   1988
Limited edition of 6,000
A *Guild* exclusive.

QUEEN VICTORIA
Designed by Stan Taylor
D6788   Large   1988
Limited edition of 3,000 exclusive to the Guild in
1988. Entered the general range in a different
colourway in 1989–1991.

GULLIVER

Designed by David Biggs

D6560	Large	1962-1967
D6563	Small	1962-1967
D6566	Mini	1962-1967

Gulliver from *Gulliver's Travels* (1726) by Jonathan Swift. This satire, like *Robinson Crusoe*, has been altered and abridged to become a children's story. In the original, Gulliver is a traveller in a fantasy of strange lands and peoples. All his experiences served to illustrate the foolishness of man and his institutions. Kings, politicians, religious leaders, scientists and philosophers are all shown in a ridiculous light, but contained in an amusing adventurous tale. This jug shows Gulliver after his shipwreck on the island of Lilliput where the diminutive inhabitants are nevertheless full of their own importance and tie down the 'giant' by his hair.

THE HAMPSHIRE CRICKETER •
D 6739
Specially Commissioned from
Royal Doulton •
by
© HAMPSHIRE C C C 1985
Celebrating 100 years of
County Cricket at Southampton
Hand Modelled and Hand Decorated
Designed by *Harry Sales*
Modelled by *GTongue*
WORLDWIDE LIMITED EDITION OF 5 000
THIS IS NUMBER 1070

THE HAMPSHIRE COUNTY CRICKET CLUB

Southampton, U.K.

THE HAMPSHIRE CRICKETER

Designed by Harry Sales

D6739   Mid size 5½"   1985

Modelled by Graham Tongue

Limited edition of 5,000, numbered with certificate. Issued in June 1985 to commemorate the centenary of county cricket at Southampton (1885-1985) and on the occasion of a four-day match with the visiting Australian team.

HENRY VIII AND HIS WIVES

HENRY VIII

Designed by Eric Griffiths

D6642	Large	1979-
D6647	Small	1979-
D6648	Mini	1979-1991

Henry VIII (1491-1547) was a monarch in the grand manner. Scholar, musician, 'Defender of the Faith', power politician and founder of the English navy, he reigned for thirty-eight years. During that time he embarked upon a tedious series of matrimonial adventures, endeavouring to provide a male heir for his dynasty. His son, Edward, became king at the age of nine, but reigned only six years after his father. However, his daughter Elizabeth, who reigned for forty-four years, proved 'a chip off the old block'.

KING HENRY VIII SECOND VERSION

Designed by Bill Harper

D6888   Large   1991

A double handled jug with the six wives modelled on the handles. The first loving cup since *Churchill* in 1940. To commemorate the 500th anniversary of his birth. Numbered Special Backstamp

Fit for a King series.

CATHERINE OF ARAGON

Designed by Alan Maslankowski

D6643	Large	1975-1989
D6657	Small	1981-1989
D6658	Mini	1981-1989

Catherine of Aragon (1485-1536).
Married 1509. Divorced 1533.

This Spanish princess was formerly married at 16 to Henry's brother Arthur, then 14. Arthur died six months after the wedding and, as it was a political marriage to unite England Spain, the young widow of 17 was then married to Henry, aged 12. This union lasted for twenty-four years and in that time she bore six children, but only one, a daughter Mary, lived. When she was in her forties and Henry could see no chance of a male heir, he divorced her and in doing so displeased the Pope and was excommunicated. Banished from court, she spent her last years in sorrow and loneliness but rarely complained. She died, aged 50, and Henry did not attend her funeral.

Noke did an interesting vellum study of Ellen Terry playing this tragic character in Shakespeare's *Henry VIII*. It was later included in the H.N. range.

ANNE BOLEYN

Designed by Douglas Tootle

D6644	Large	1975-1990
D6650	Small	1980-1990
D665l	Mini	1980-1990

Anne Boleyn (1507-1536).
Married 1533. Executed 1536.

The daughter of a nobleman, and educated in France, Anne was vivacious and captivating, and a lady-in-waiting to the solemn Catherine. Henry was infatuated with her and loved her passionately. He decorated Hampton Court Palace with their entwined initials in lovers' knots. She presented him with a daughter Elizabeth and miscarried a son. Three years after the marriage she was accused of infidelity and taken to the Tower of London where, at the age of 29, she had her head struck off her unusually long neck by a French swordsman. In error, the designer used an executioner's axe for the handle of this jug.

JANE SEYMOUR

Designed by Michael Abberley
D6646   Large   1979-1990
D6746   Small   1986-1990
D6747   Mini   1986-1990

Jane Seymour (1509?-1537). Married 1536.

Also a nobleman's daughter in the service of
Queen Catherine, and later Anne Boleyn. Jane
was as calm, meek and gentle as Anne was
not. She married Henry ten days after Anne's
execution and she bore him a son in the next
year, so that Henry's throne was secured in the
twenty-ninth year of his reign. The christening
was an elaborate and happy occasion, with
Mary and Elizabeth attending their baby brother, and the troubles of the past seemed
mended. However, the birth and baptismal celebrations proved too much for the Queen and
she died twelve days after her son was born. She was lovingly remembered and was the
only one of his queens to be buried at Henry's side. It is significant that Henry waited two
years before remarrying.

ANNE OF CLEVES

Designed by Michael Abberley
D6653   Large   1980-1990
D6753   Small   1987-1990
D6754   Mini   1987-1990

Anne of Cleves (1515-1557).
Married 1540. Divorced 1540.

His ministers decided on another political
marriage to a foreign princess and Henry,
deluded by a flattering portrait of Anne of
Cleves by Holbein, invited her to England to be
his wife. On seeing her in the flesh he named
her 'The Flanders Mare' and, as the political
situation had changed, he hastily had the
marriage annulled. Henceforth he referred to her as his 'sister', gave her an income and a
manor where she lived comfortably and happily until she died from natural causes ten years
after Henry's death.

When first issued in 1980 the ears of the horse on the handle were erect but in later
models the design was modified so that the ears were less prone to damage.

The small size was modelled by Peter Gee.

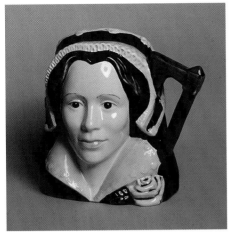

CATHERINE HOWARD

Designed by Peter Gee

D6645	Large	1978-1989
D6692	Small	1984-1989
D6693	Mini	1984-1989

Catherine Howard (1521-1542).
Married 1540. Executed 1542.

High spirited and a bright-eyed charmer like her cousin Anne Boleyn, Catherine was married by the connivance of ambitious relatives, at the age of 19 to Henry nearing 50. She was adored by him, but naturally turned to companions of her own age. She would undoubtedly have led any husband a dance, but as queen in the intrigue-laden court, she should have remained above suspicion. Like her cousin, she was accused of infidelity, tried and executed at the Tower of London

CATHERINE PARR

Designed by Michael Abberley

D6664	Large	1981-1989
D6751	Small	1986-1989
D6752	Mini	1986-1989

Catherine Parr (1512-1548). Married 1543.

For his sixth and last venture into matrimony, Henry chose a very different Catherine. At 31 she was twice widowed, educated and accomplished, sensitive and sympathetic. She was wife, and nurse to Henry, now an 'irascible man-mountain'. She cared for all his children and reconciled the two princesses with their father. She created harmony and cleverly lived to survive Henry. She then married for a fourth time the man whom she had intended to be her third husband, the dashing Thomas Seymour. However, she died (like her sister-in-law Jane Seymour) soon after bearing him a child.

The prayer stool handle is more suited to the character of the first Catherine. In fact all the queens in this set appear a little too severe to please the indulgent Henry.

THE HEROES OF THE BLITZ

Designed by Stan Taylor

D6872	A.R.P. Warden	Small	1991
D6886	Home Guard	Small	1991
D6887	Auxiliary Fireman	Small	1991

Commissioned by *Lawleys by Post*
To celebrate the 50th anniversary of the formation of the Local Defence Volunteers in May 1940. Edition of 9,500.

Heroes of the Blitz – During the Second World War all able bodied men were conscripted into the Armed Forces. This meant a shortage of manpower on the Home Front. This gap was ably filled by part timers made up of those too young or old to be *called up,* those deferred on medical grounds and those in reserved occupations.

A.R.P. Wardens shepherded the public into shelters during air raids, saw that blackout restrictions were observed and fire watched for incendiary bombs etc. The whistle on the handle was his way of sounding the alert.

The Home Guard, made very familiar today to T.V. viewers in *Dad's Army* prepared to intercept the enemy should they invade. The handle is a sten gun and a grenade.

Auxiliary Fireman assisted the main Fire Service in putting out the many fires caused in the cities by incendiary bombs from the air. Handle hose and brass nozzle.

You (Hitler) do your worst and we will do our best
Speech at Civil Defence Services luncheon on 14.7.1941 by Winston Churchill

THE HEROIC LEADERS

Designed by Stan Taylor

D6849	SIR WINSTON CHURCHILL	Small	1989
D6850	VISCOUNT MONTGOMERY OF ALAMEIN	Small	1989
D6851	EARL MOUNTBATTEN OF BURMA	Small	1989

Commissioned by *Lawleys by Post*

To celebrate the 50th anniversary of the Second World War and of the men who helped to win it. An edition of 9,500. Three small size jugs made in two-part moulds incorporating the handle in one with the body. Micro transfers used for badge and epaulette details. Numbered and certificate.

SIR WINSTON CHURCHILL (1874-1965)
Handle – Union Jack.
Winston Churchill took over the leadership of a coalition government and the country in 1940. His strong personality guided the whole nation through six difficult years of war. His inspired wartime speeches and V-sign gave hope to millions all over the world.

VISCOUNT MONTGOMERY OF ALAMEIN (1887-1976)
Handle – Army standard.
A professional soldier and brilliant strategist. Although imperious he was able to inspire his men with his own confidence and they respected him. His victories in North Africa were the first of the war and he went on to command victorious British armies until he received the German surrender at Luneberg. Eccentric in his dress he wears the ordinary soldier's battledress blouse and a Tank Corp beret with two badges.

EARL MOUNTBATTEN OF BURMA (1900-1979)
Handle – White Ensign of the Royal Navy.
A grandson of Queen Victoria, he began the war as captain of a destroyer, *H.M.S. Kelly*. He almost lost his life when it sank off Crete. He was responsible for the allied landings in North Africa in 1942. He became Commander-in-Chief South East Asia 1943-6 and turned the tide to victory at Imphal, Assam and drove the Japanese out of Burma. Only the Japanese surrender halted the advance.

THE HIGBEE COMPANY
(Department Store) Cleveland, Ohio, U.S.A.

MAD HATTER
D6748   Large   1985

Limited edition of 250 to celebrate the opening of the Doulton Room. A new colourway of a discontinued jug, it sold out on the opening day – 28th October 1985.

OLD CHARLEY
D6761   Large   1986

Limited edition of 250 to celebrate the first anniversary of the opening. A new colourway of a discontinued jug, it had a black hat and a maroon jacket.

MAD HATTER
D6790   Small   1987

OLD CHARLEY
D6791   Small   1987

Limited edition of 500 copies in the above colourways to celebrate the second anniversary of the opening. Sold as a pair only.

CHELSEA PENSIONER
D6832   Large   1988

Limited edition of 250 to celebrate the third anniversary of the opening. A new design by Stan Taylor, which entered the general range in January 1989. Also issued to *Holmes, Horne* and *Strawbridge & Clothier* under their own backstamp.

ELEPHANT TRAINER
D6841   Large   1989

Limited edition of 250 to celebrate the fourth anniversary of the opening. A new design which entered the general range in 1990. Also issued to *Holmes, Horne* and *Strawbridge & Clothier* under their own backstamps.

D.H. HOLMES
(Department Store)
New Orleans, U.S.A.

LONG JOHN SILVER
D6799   Large   1987

Limited edition of 250 to celebrate the first anniversary the opening of the Doulton Room. A new colourway of a current jug with an orchid brown coat and a green hat.

CHELSEA PENSIONER
D6831   Large   1988

Limited edition of 250 to celebrate the first anniversary of the Doulton Room. A new design by Stan Taylor which entered the general range in January 1989. Also issued to *Higbee, Horne* and *Strawbridge & Clothier* under their own backstamps.

ELEPHANT TRAINER
D6841   Large   1989

Limited edition of 250 to celebrate the second anniversary of the opening. A new design which entered the general range in 1990. Also issued to *Higbee, Horne* and *Strawbridge & Clothier* under their own backstamps.

The limited number of jugs (250) and the issue price place these jugs out of the reach of most collectors.

ROBIN HOOD
Designed by Harry Fenton

D6205	Large	1947-1960
D6234	Small	1947-1960
D6252	Mini	1947-1960

Robin Hood – Robin of Locksley – was born c.1160, but the stories woven about his name are mainly legend. They tell of Robin Hood, a nobleman whom when disinherited, lived in the shelter of Sherwood Forest, Nottingham. There he led a band of outlaws, who robbed rich travellers to feed the poor and persecuted, taking the lives of only the most persistent enemies and always showing courtesy to women. This dashing, romantic figure, the hero of many stories and ballads, gave Douglas Fairbanks, 1924, and Errol Flynn, 1938, and many since one of their best cinematic roles.

ROBIN HOOD
SECOND VERSION
(WITH BOW HANDLE)

Designed by Max Henk

D6527	Large	1960-1992
D6534	Small	1960-1992
D6541	Mini	1960-1991

Errol Flynn in *The Adventures of Robin Hood.* 1938

Under the Greenwood Tree Seriesware Burslem 1914-1967

65

CAPTAIN HOOK

Designed by Max Henk and David Biggs

D6597	Large	1965-1971
D6601	Small	1965-1971
D6605	Mini	1965-1971

CAPTAIN HOOK
SECOND VERSION

Designed by Martyn Alcock

D6947   Large   1994

Character Jug of the Year
Handle – crocodile and hook.
A donation to *Great Ormond Street Hospital for Sick Children* will be made for every jug sold.
The film *Hook* was released in the U.K. in 1993.

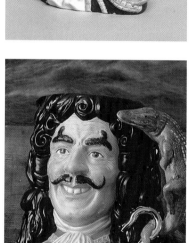

Captain Hook, from *Peter Pan* (1904) by J.M. Barrie, is the villain of the story. He wishes to be revenged against Peter Pan as it was he who cut off Hook's arm and fed it to a passing crocodile. This beast, which forms the handle of the jugs, has its tail curled around a clock in the early version 'The crocodile' says Hook, 'liked my arm so much that it has followed me ever since ...licking its lips for the rest of me... That crocodile would have had me before this, but by a lucky chance it swallowed a clock which goes "tick tick" inside it, and so before it can reach me I hear the tick and bolt'. The crocodile got him in the end!

JOSEPH HORNE
(Department Store) Pittsburgh, U.S.A.

FALCONER D6798   Large   1987
Limited edition of 250 to celebrate the opening of the Doulton Room in November 1987.
A new colourway of a current jug with a dark brown coat and a dark green hat.

CHELSEA PENSIONER D6830   Large   1988
Limited edition of 250 to celebrate the first anniversary of the Doulton Room. A new version by Stan Taylor which entered the general range in January 1989. Also issue to *Higbee, Holmes* and *Strawbridge & Clothier* under their own backstamps.

ELEPHANT TRAINER D6841   Large   1989
Limited edition of 250 to celebrate the second anniversary of the opening. A new design which entered the general range in 1990. Also issued to *Higbee, Holmes* and *Strawbridge & Clothier* under their own backstamps.

SIR LEONARD HUTTON

Designed by Stan Taylor
D6945   Small   1993

Commissioned by *Lawleys by Post* in an edition of 9,500.

Len Hutton (1916-1990) was one of the greatest batsmen of all time. His record innings of 364 is recorded on the handle of the jug and was made playing Australia at the Oval in 1938. He was knighted in 1956 and in 1990 became President of Yorkshire Cricket Club for whom he had played. He wears his Yorkshire cap with the white rose of York. Jug No. 1 was presented to the Duchess of Kent who despite her title is from Yorkshire. She is patron of the *Sir Leonard Hutton 364 Appeal* to provide sporting facilities for young people. A donation will be made to the appeal for every jug sold.

JARGE

Designed by Harry Fenton
D6288   Large   1950-1960
D6295   Small   1950-1960

As the dialect version of George, the titling of this jug suggests that this character belongs to the country. With the spotted neckerchief and his chewing on a straw, he may look a bit of a simpleton, but he is master of country matters and, as the entwined hearts on the jug suggest, a 'bit of a lad' with the milkmaids.

THOMAS JEFFERSON

Designed by Stan Taylor
D6943   Large   1994

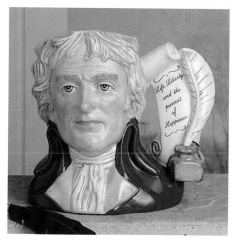

To commemorate the 250th anniversary of his birth in 1743.

The second jug in *The Presidential Series*. Only on sale in the U.S. in a limited edition of 2,500.

Thomas Jefferson (1743-1826) was largely responsible for drafting that great piece of eloquence, *The Declaration of Independence* here used as the handle. He was born in Virginia, became its Governor in 1779, Ambassador to Paris 1785, and finally the Third President of the United States 1801-9. He was responsible for the *Louisiana Purchase* when the U.S bought the French Colonial Territory in North America. Above all he was a country gentleman who introduced English landscape gardening into America. Of no religious denomination he was noted for his liberal policy and educational and humanitarian reforms.

We hold these truths to be self evident,
That all men are created equal,
That they are endowed by their creator with certain unalienable rights,
That among these are life, liberty and the pursuit of happiness.

JESTER

Designed by Charles Noke
D5556   Small   1936-1960
D6953   Tiny   1994
D6111   Wall Pocket   1940-1960
D6910   Small Toby   1992-1993

The jester – a familiar figure in wealthy medieval households – given much licence to entertain. He amused the company with songs, stories and amusing repartee. He is a close relative of the clown and was often employed in Shakespeare's plays as light relief.

JOCKEY

Designed by David Biggs
D6625   Large   1971-1975
D6229   Small   1974 Pilot

This jockey has the lean look of a champion who has passed the winning post in first place many times in his long career. He wears red, yellow and green silks in his owner's colours.

Small size Pilot Jugs are known.

JOCKEY
SECOND VERSION

Designed by Stan Taylor
D6877   Small   1991-1994

One of the series of eight small size sporting subjects issued in 1990 and 1991.

This jug has a younger leaner jockey and the horse joins him at the winning post handle.

FARMER JOHN

Designed by Charles Noke
D5788   Large   1938-1960
D5789   Small   1938-1960
D6007   Ash Bowl   1939-1960

Early versions of this jug have an 'inside' handle.

This cheerful jug, modelled in the same traditional manner as *John Barleycorn*, shows a merry Farmer John . A countryman who rises early, *ploughs and sows, reaps and mows*, but finally enjoys a well earned pint of cider, a product of his own orchards.

SAMUEL JOHNSON
Designed by Harry Fenton
D6289   Large   1950-1960
D6296   Small   1950-1960

Samuel Johnson (1709-1784) published *A Dictionary of the English Language* in 1755.
He was the outstanding literary figure of the eighteenth century.
A celebrated conversationalist and clubman, his circle included many of the most brilliant figures of his age. A favourite meeting place 'The Cheshire Cheese' in Fleet Street, London, still prospers today.

There is nothing which has yet been contrived by man, by which so much happiness is produced, as by a good tavern or inn.

Dr Johnson at the Cheshire Cheese plaque Burslem 1938-1952

PETER JONES (CHINA) LTD
20-22 Little Westgate, Wakefield, Yorkshire WF1 1LE

FALCONER
D6800   Large   1987
Limited edition of 1,000. A new colourway of a current jug with maroon and cream striped hat.

ATHOS
D6827   Large   1988
PORTHOS
D6828   Large   1988
ARAMIS
D6829   Large   1988
Limited edition of 1,000.
New colourways.

JUGGLER

Designed by Stan Taylor
D6835   Large   1989-1992

The Juggler practices a dexterous balancing act with his clubs and is included in the collection of the four *Circus Performers*.

KEVIN FRANCIS CERAMICS LTD

Kevin Pearson /Francis Salmon,
85 Landcroft Road, London SE22 9BR.

'The Collecting World' a series of three jugs. An original creation by Kevin Pearson and Geoff Blower, and modelled by Stan Taylor.

THE COLLECTOR

D6796   Large   1988
D6906   Small   1991
Limited edition of 1,500.

THE ANTIQUE DEALER

D6807   Large   1988

THE AUCTIONEER

D6838   Large   1989
Limited edition of 5,000 each. Certificate.

Commissioned by *Kevin Francis Ceramics Ltd.* in a Limited edition of 5,000.

The interesting handles are on the left. *The Collector's* handle is formed from a *Mephistopheles* character jug so that one gets two jugs in one and an expensive one at that. The second incorporates a silver candlestick and a seventeenth-century flintlock pistol. The third has that popular figurine *The Bather* HN687. What a shame a suitable Doulton piece couldn't be found for the second character.

Roger Davis at Knotting was the model for the *Auctioneer*.

THE PENDLE WITCH

Designed by Stan Taylor
D6826   Large   1989

LAWLEYS BY POST

Minton House, London Road, Stoke-on-Trent. Royal Doulton's mail order outlet.

THE DICKENS TINIES

Set of 12 to celebrate the 170th anniversary of Dickens' birth, 1982

SLEUTH

D6773   Small   1987   5,000
Commemorating the centenary of the first Sherlock Holmes story *A Study in Scarlet* 1887. New colourway of current jug with red coat.

QUEEN ELIZABETH/KING PHILIP

Designed by Bill Harper
D6821/2 Small   1988   9,500
Lawleys in association with the Maritime Museum, Greenwich, to celebrate the 400th anniversary of the defeat of the Spanish Armada in 1588. The jugs, numbered and with certificate, sold as pairs – the handles being on opposite sides.

JOURNEY THROUGH BRITAIN

Designed by Stan Taylor and 'depicting people in typically British occupations'

THE POSTMAN	D6801	1988
THE ENGINE DRIVER	D6823	1988
THE FIREMAN	D6839	1989
THE POLICEMAN	D6852	1990

Small limited edition of 5,000
Numbered and with certificate, these attractive and detailed jugs also have exceptionally good backstamps.

W.G. GRACE

Designed by Stan Taylor
D6845   Small   1989   9,500

THE HEROIC LEADERS

Designed by Stan Taylor
D6849 SIR WINSTON CHURCHILL
D6850 VISCOUNT MONTGOMERY OF ALEMAIN
D6851 EARL MOUNTBATTEN OF BURMA
          Small   1989   9,500

HEROES OF THE BLITZ

Designed by Stan Taylor
D6872   A.R.P. WARDEN
D6886   HOME GUARD
D6887   AUXILIARY FIREMAN
          Small   1991   9,500

SIR LEONARD HUTTON

Designed by Stan Taylor
D6945   Small   1993   9,500

CHARLIE CHAPLIN

AS 'THE LITTLE TRAMP'
Designed by Bill Harper
D6949   Large   1993   5,000

MR. PICKWICK

Designed by Bill Harper
D6959   Large   1994   2,500
First jug with metal accessory – the spectacles. All the above only available by mail order.

LAWYER

Designed by Max Henk

D6498	Large	1959-
D6504	Small	1959-
D6524	Mini	1960-1991
D6504	Table Lighter	1962-1974

This is one of many jugs in the range with a quill pen for a handle, and it suggests that this lawyer is from a bygone age. However, he looks far too genial for most of the lawyers portrayed in Dickens' novels. In England today lawyers still wear horsehair wigs, cravats and the gowns of Queen Anne's day to illustrate the ancient roots of their profession.

No poet ever interpreted nature as freely as a lawyer interprets truth.

Giradoux.

LEPRECHAUN

Designed by Bill Harper

D6847	Large	1991-
D6899	Small	1992-

Pre-released in a limited edition of 50 by *Site of the Green* , Dundas, Ontario, Canada, in 1990 and 1991 with special backstamp.

D6948   Smally Toby   1994-

The Leprechaun is a solitary Irish fairy traditionally a shoe-maker. He has great wealth and if you can catch and hold him he will yield it to you but is also renowned as a slippery customer. Incorporated in this jug is the legend that a pot of gold is to be found at the rainbow's end so that it owes more to the Broadway musical and film of *Finian's Rainbow.* Apparently Pat O'Brian of Royal Doulton, Canada suggested the rainbow and it makes a novel handle. Both Pat and the owner of *Site of the Green,* who pre-released The Leprechaun have Irish roots.

ABRAHAM LINCOLN

Designed by Stan Taylor
D6936   Large   1992

The first jug in *The Presidential Series*.

Limited edition of 2,500 for sale in the United States only. Handle formed by the Union Flag and the Gettysburg Address.

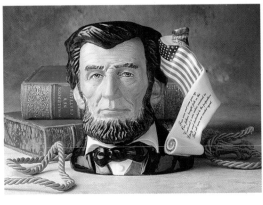

Abraham Lincoln (1809-1865) was born in Kentucky to an illiterate family. Self-educated he became a practising lawyer in 1837. A skillful orator and known for his integrity he rose to become the Sixteenth President of the United States in 1861. His known views on anti-slavery precipitated the secession of the seven Southern States from the Union. Lincoln worked to preserve the Union at all costs. In 1863 he proclaimed the freedom of the slaves in the Confederate States and gave the Gettysburg Address. He advocated a reconciliatory policy towards the South at the end of the war. *With malice towards none, with charity for all.*
He was shot whilst attending a performance at *Ford's Theatre* in Washington.

The Government of the People, by the People, for the People shall not perish from the earth.

LOBSTER MAN

Designed by David Biggs
D6617   Large   1968-1991
D6620   Small   1968-1992
D6651   Mini   1980-1991
D6783   Large   1987-1989 New colourway

The lobster man works the shallow seas around the shore, sinking his baskets in spots likely to be the haunt of the lobster. Each day, in all weathers, he laboriously hauls out the 'pots' to discover his catch. If he is lucky he will carry off his haul and boil them until they become the bright, familiar red of those enjoyed at our tables.

LONDON BOBBY

Designed by Stan Taylor
D6744   Large   1986-
D6762   Small   1987-
D6763   Mini   1987-1991

The *Bobby* is named after Sir Robert Peel who founded the modern police force in 1828. This popular character, translated as a jug, has proved to be a best seller; sometimes selling up to four times more than any other jug. Being such a typically London character he is probably bought by the many tourists who visit London as much as by the dedicated Doulton collector. At first the hat badge was embossed and hand-painted, but in late 1987 all three versions were given a transfer badge. The handle is formed by Big Ben's clock tower as used on the John Doulton jug. I wish it could have been given a different time.

Ev'ry member of the force
has a watch and chain, of course;
if you want to know the time,
ask a p'liceman!

          E.W. Rodders.

LORD MAYOR OF LONDON

Designed by Stan Taylor
D6864   Large   1990

Handle is City sceptre whose head is fifteenth century and the shaft is possibly Saxon.

The first Mayor of the City of London assumed office in 1191, and the first Lord Mayor in 1283. He is elected annually by his fellow Aldermen, Sheriffs and Members of the City Livery Companies (Guilds).

In the City he takes precedence over everyone including Royal princes. The reigning sovereign still

receives the City sword from and returns it to the Lord Mayor before crossing the boundary at Temple Bar. The Lord Mayor rides in a magnificent golden coach when celebrating his inauguration in November.

LONG JOHN SILVER

Designed by Max Henk

D6335	Large	1952-
D6386	Small	1960-
D6512	Mini	1960-1991
D6386	Table Lighter	1958-1973
D6799	Large	1987

see *D.H. Holmes* new colourway.

Long John Silver from *Treasure Island* (1883) by Robert Louis Stevenson. This rascally leader of a pirate band has a wooden leg and a parrot companion named after his old master, Captain Flint. A plausible rogue, he gains the confidence of the boy hero of the story, Jim Hawkins, and his friends when they set sail in their ship the *Hispaniola* in search of Flint's lost treasure.

Fifteen men on the dead man's chest –
Yo-ho-ho, and a bottle of rum!
Drink and the Devil had done for the rest –
Yo-ho-ho, and a bottle of rum!

LUMBERJACK

Designed by Max Henk

D6610	Large	1967-1983
D6613	Small	1967-1983
D	Mini	1983

A Miniature size was made and appears on the market from time to time. They are not as rare as reported.

Special backstamp in 1967, when sold only in Northern America:
'Canadian Centennial Series 1867-1967'
(See *North American Indian* and *Trapper*).

The counterpart of this North American character is found in many countries. He is always a tough, hardy individual, used to hard work in difficult terrain, and often living in lumber camps under harsh conditions for months on end.

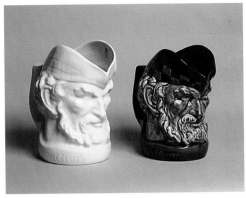

D. & J. MCCALLUM
(Distillers) Edinburgh, Scotland

THE MCCALLUM

D269   Large   Kingsware Glaze   1930
1,000-1,500 issued

D270   Large   Ivory Glaze   1930
1,000 issued

These details appearing in the Doulton design book for advertising wares inform us that the Ivory Glaze (their term) version is rarer than the Kingsware. The design has McCallum's copyright and other firms, including Wade, made very similar jugs with only slight mould differences. Small sizes were made but never by Doulton. The Doulton version of this jug has been much abused by faking in recent years, but if you remember that the body of a Kingsware jug is always terracotta you can't go wrong. Also remember a McCallum would never sport the Gordon tartan some ivory versions have been seen to wear!

However, an unrecorded but genuine version has surfaced recently with a treacle glaze over a white body and a distinct green glaze on hat, handle and collar. It seems there will always be new variations discovered.

MAD HATTER
Designed by Max Henk
D6598   Large   1965-1983
D6602   Small   1965-1983
D6606   Mini   1965-1983

See Special Commissions – Higbee.

The Mad Hatter from *Alice's Adventures in Wonderland* (1865) by Lewis Carroll. It was always teatime at the March Hare's house. Alice, coming upon the tea party in the garden, sat down uninvited. The other guests were the Mad Hatter, wearing an item from his stock – a top hat with a large price ticket attached – and the Dormouse who forms the handle of this jug. The Dormouse was usually asleep despite the Hatter pouring hot tea on its nose to keep it awake. The Hatter's watch, also shown, told the months of the year rather than the hours. It kept very bad time due to the crumbs in its works put there when the March Hare, trying to improve things, buttered it with the breadknife. Even a rinse in a cup of tea didn't help!

MAORI

D6080   Large   1939

Two prototypes were made of this jug but the pilot copies recorded are of the version shown here.

The Pilot jugs were circulated before the Second World War but never put into production because of it. One was left with the *Shorter* company in Sydney and one it is said was inadvertently sold in a retail shop in London.

Maoris are the native inhabitants of New Zealand. They are an attractive race of Polynesian character, tall, vigorous and brave. Some traditional facial tattoos are shown on the jug.

A prototype was modelled with an Alice handle. This jug was issued in a new series of three 'Alice' characters.

THE MARCH HARE

Designed by Bill Harper
D6776   Large   1989-1991

A new departure for Doulton, this is the first animal character ever used in the range, although lots have formed handles. Lewis Carroll's original March Hare was a rather bad-tempered, humourless and pedantic character; this jug is a much nicer character with a nicely crazed expression suitable to a mad March Hare although Alice had hoped, 'he might not be so mad as it was May.' It was the March Hare who gave the 'mad' tea-party at his house to which Alice invited herself. The dormouse tells a story at the tea-party about *'three little sisters, Elsie, Lacie and Tillie'*. These were the names of the three Liddell sisters.

'It's the stupidest tea-party I was ever at in all my life!'

THE MASTER

Designed by Stan Taylor
D6898   Small   1991

One of a series of eight sporting subjects
issued in the small size only in 1990-1991.
U.S. title *The Equestrian.*

The Master of the hunt looks a very fine figure
and probably enjoys his gallop through the
fields with his company but the final result of
the tearing to pieces of a terrified fox by a pack
of hounds is not such a fine picture. This is
one character I wish was historical rather than
reflecting popular modern interests as the
Doulton brochure says.

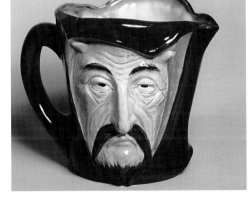

MEPHISTOPHELES

Designed by Charles Noke and Harry
Fenton
D5757   Large   1937-1948
D5758   Small   1937-1948

This is the only double-sided jug in the
range until the introduction of 'The
Antagonists' collection in 1983.

Some copies have the following verse
printed on the base.

When the devil was sick,
The devil a saint would be.
When the devil got well,
devil a saint was he.
                    Samuel Smiles

This name for the Devil or evil spirit will
always be associated with the drama
Faust.

Noke designed a double-sided
Mephistopheles matchstriker in the 1890s
which was obviously the inspiration for
this jug. At the same time he produced his
Janus figure in vellum of Mephistopheles
and Marguerite as they appeared in *Faust.*

MERLIN

Designed by Garry Sharpe

D6529	Large	1960-
D6536	Small	1960-
D6543	Mini	1960-1991

Merlin, a Celtic god. It was said that it was with his powers that the stones of Stonehenge were brought from Ireland to be arranged in their circle where he was worshiped. He is more usually associated with Arthurian legend and represented as the enchanter who becomes Arthur's counsellor and aids him by magic. Merlin created the round table around which Arthur and his knights met, thus, a pagan deity was incorporated into Christian legend, but the owl handle refers to a darker age.

MR. MICAWBER

Designed by Charles Noke with the later models by Harry Fenton

D5843	Mid Size	1938-1948
D5843	Small	1948-1960
D6138	Mini	1940-1960
D6143	Tiny	1940-1960
HN1615	Bookend	1936-c. 1939
M58	Napkin Ring	c. 1935-1939
D6050	Bust	1939-1960
D6262	Toby Jug – Small	1948-1960
D5843	Table Lighter	1958

Mr. Micawber from *David Copperfield* (1849) by Charles Dickens.
Wilkins Micawber, with whom David lodges on first coming to London, moves optimistically from employment to employment endeavouring to support his wife and ever increasing family. He is hopelessly improvident, but always confident that 'something will turn up'. He tells David,

'My other piece of advice, Copperfield, you know, Annual income twenty pounds, annual expenditure nineteen nineteen six, result happiness. Annual income twenty pounds, annual expenditure twenty pounds ought and six, result misery.'

THE MIKADO

Designed by Max Henk

D6501	Large	1959-1969
D6507	Small	1959-1969
D6525	Mini	1960-1969

The Mikado – this title of the Emperor of Japan was popularised by Gilbert and Sullivan's comic opera of that name, which opened in London and New York in 1885. In the play the Mikado is the absolute autocrat, with power of life and death over his subjects and, in particular, the hero and the heroine of the piece. The plot hinges on this fact.

Our great Mikado, virtuous man,
So he decreed in words succinct
That all who flirted, leered or winked
(Unless connubially linked),
Should forthwith be beheaded

GLEN MILLER

Designed by Bill Harper
D6970   Large   1994

His famous gold rimmed glasses are represented in metal.
1994 is the 50th anniversary of his disapppearance on a flight between England and France.

Glen Miller (1904-1944), the famous band leader and trombonist who created the *big band sound*. He composed his signature tune *Moonlight Serenade* and *In the Mood*. He enlisted and his orchestra entertained the Armed Forces during the Second World War.

Special Backstamp for 1994.

MINE HOST

Designed by Max Henk

D6468	Large	1958-1982
D6470	Small	1958-1982
D6513	Mini	1960-1982

Our cheerful landlord is the ancestor of today's publican. On the handle is the evergreen bough one of the earliest signs which, when hung outside a house, told the traveller that refreshment was within. Beneath it is displayed a tun of extra strong ale to further tempt the thirsty man.

Have ye tippled drink more fine
Than mine host's canary wine?
Or are the fruits of Paradise
Sweeter than those dainty pies
of venison?

Keats

MONTY

Designed by Harry Fenton
D6202   Large   1946-1991
Yellow details, discontinued 1954.

Field Marshal Montgomery (1887-1976) was egotistical and a great individualist, as many great leaders have been. Although a martinet, he was loved and respected by his men who referred to him familiarly as 'Monty'. He affected the simple beret and battledress of the Tank Corp throughout his campaigns. Monty led the first Allied victory of the Second World War in North Africa in 1942 and, in 1945 at his Luneberg headquarters, he accepted the surrender of the North-West German forces. He became a peer of the realm and a well loved public figure.

This sort of thing may be tolerated by the French but we are British, thank God.
Comment on the Homosexuality Bill, 1965.

MONTGOMERY OF ALAMEIN

Designed by Stan Taylor
D6908   Large   1992
Limited edition of 2,500

Monty is shown as the general who fought at El Alamein.

In defeat unbeatable; in victory unbearable
Churchill on Montgomery

Before Alamein we never had a victory, After Alamein we never had a defeat.
Winston Churchill

Also see *Heroic Leaders*

SIR THOMAS MORE

Designed by Stan Taylor
D6792   Large   1988-1991

More (1478-2535) was a brilliant scholar, lawyer and writer, a friend of Erasmus and a patron of the arts. Holbein lived in his house in Chelsea for three years. He wrote many works in Latin and English, his most famous being *Utopia* which gave a new word to the English language. The land he wrote of had communistic ideals, equal education and opportunity for men and women and religious tolerance. The book was immediately popular and translated into five languages.

Became Lord Chancellor to Henry VIII in 1529 and Henry showed him great favour until Sir Thomas found he could not condone Henry electing himself head of the church, impugning the Pope and divorcing Catherine of Aragon. More was consequently imprisoned in the Tower and executed. His head was exhibited on London Bridge.

I like him most for his education of his daughters who became scholars and liberated women. His daughter, Margaret Roper purchased his head and preserved it in spices until at her own death it was buried with her. I think the handle is far too 'churchy' for this great man, so lively and forward thinking.

That we may merrily meet in Heaven.
Sir Thomas More's last letter to Margaret Roper.

CAPTAIN HENRY MORGAN

Designed by Garry Sharpe
D6467   Large   1958-1982
D6469   Small   1958-1882
D6510   Mini   1960-1982

Captain Henry Morgan (1635-1688) was the
most famous buccaneer of the Spanish Main
who plundered the Spanish possessions in the
West Indies for the British. In 1671 he capture
Panama. Born in South Wales, he was
transported from the port of Bristol as a young
man, to became a plantation worker in
Barbados. However, after many adventures he
became Lieutenant-Governor of Jamaica and
was knighted by King Charles II. His life story reads like lurid Hollywood fiction and in fact
he was the model for many swashbuckling heroes of the cinema.

EARL MOUNTBATTEN OF BURMA

Designed by Stan Taylor
D6944   Large   1993

Commissioned by *R.D.I.C.C.*
In a limited edition of 5,000.

Louis Mountbatten, 1st Earl Mountbatten of
Burma (1900-1979), cousin to Queen
Elizabeth II and uncle to Prince Phillip was
affectionately known as *Uncle Dicky* by the
Royal family. He served in the Navy during
two World Wars. See *Heroic Leaders* for his
exploits in the second. In 1947 he was
appointed the last Viceroy of India and
performed the difficult task of transferring
power to India and Pakistan whilst retaining
the friendship and respect of both. He served
as First Sea Lord and Chief of Naval Staff, 1955-1959. He had a typical wry humour and
was a popular national figure. Much more handsome than his jug in my opinion. Lord Louis
was assassinated by an I.R.A. bomb whilst yachting with his family in Ireland in 1979.
He is shown in Naval dress uniform.

THE MUSKETEERS

ATHOS
Designed by Max Henk

D6439	Large	1956-1991
D6452	Small	1956-1991
D6509	Mini	1960-1991

ARAMIS
Designed by Max Henk

D6441	Large	1956-1991
D6454	Small	1956-1991
D6508	Mini	1960-1991

D'ARTAGNAN
Designed by Stan Taylor

D6691	Large	1982-
D6764	Small	1987-
D6765	Mini	1987-1991

PORTHOS
Designed by Max Henk

D6440	Large	1956-1991
D6453	Small	1956-1911
D6516	Mini	1960-1991
D6453	Table Lighter	1958

Early backstamps of *Athos, Aramis* and *Porthos* state *One of the three Musketeers.*
See *Peter Jones* for set in new colourway. 1988.

Aramis, Athos and Porthos are the Musketeers of *The Three Musketeers* by Alexandre Dumas, a French romance published in 1844. These three members of Louis XIII's Musketeers befriend d'Artagnan, a young gentleman from Gascony, who comes to Paris to join their celebrated band. Together they share many heroic adventures, united by their maxim,

All for one, and one for all.

NAPOLEON

Designed by Stan Taylor
D6941   Large   1993
Limited edition of 2,000

The handle is an *eagle* standard. The eagle being sacred to Zeus was used as a standard by the Roman Legions and Napoleon adopted it for his Empire.

Napoleon (1769-1821) Like another *Little Corporal* 130 years later, rose through the Army ranks. Conquered a large part of Europe only to be defeated by over-extending his resources. Finally defeated at Waterloo by Allied Forces under Wellington, he was exiled to St. Helena where he died.

His liaisons with Josephine and Mari Louise can be read in relation to *The Antagonist Collection*. His reign as Emperor of the French is too well known for me to repeat. He was a hero to the French and also to the English, one of whose idiosyncrasies is respecting their enemies and making pottery effigies of them. Figures and jugs were made at Lambeth and other Potteries in the 1800's but never by Doulton and Watts. This is the first time Doulton have honoured *Old Boney.*

LORD NELSON

Designed by Geoff Blower
D6336   Large   1952-1969

Horatio, Viscount Nelson (1758-1805) entered the navy as a midshipman at the age of twelve. Later he was notable for his victories at the Nile (1798), Copenhagen (1801), and Trafalgar (1805) where he was killed to be mourned by a whole nation as a popular hero. His love for Emma Hamilton has caught the romantic interest of writers ever since.

TRAFALGAR

150th anniversary of the battle 1955

LORD NELSON

D6636   Large   1955

Special backstamps to commemorate the 150th anniversary of the battle on 21st October 1955, Trafalgar Day.

These copies exist with the appendages, First Sea Lord, First Lord and Secretary, which were given to the Admiralty Room, Whitehall in perpetuity.

Earl Mountbatten was the first recipient of the jug designated First Lord. Eight other jugs carrying this backstamp were made. One was given to the *Victory* Museum, Portsmouth, and remains there today in storage. Seven others were presented to Admiral Golovko and other members of the Russian Baltic Fleet in Portsmouth, during the anniversary celebrations and are now presumably in Russia.

England expects that every man will do his duty.

Nelson's signal before the Battle of Trafalgar.

VICE ADMIRAL LORD NELSON

Designed by Stan Taylor
D6932   Large   1993

Character Jug of the Year. Special backstamp and certificate.

Cape Trafalgar off Spain was the scene of Nelson's greatest victory when he defeated the combined French and Spanish fleets and captured twenty enemy ships. Unfortunately Nelson himself was mortally wounded and died three hours after the battle ended. His body was pickled in a barrel of rum and taken back to England aboard his flagship *The Victory* which forms the handle of this jug. The barrel is preserved in Whitehall and in the Navy rum is still known as *Nelson's blood*. He was buried in St. Paul's Cathedral and his funeral procession was watched by the young John Doulton on one of his few days off in 1806. Nelson was his hero and was the subject of the first character jug ever made by Doulton and Watts. Nelson is shown here in full Admirals uniform with his Nile medal and the likeness is taken from a painting by *L.F. Abbot* in the *National Maritime Museum.*

NELSON

Designed by Warren Platt
D6963   Small   1994
Commissioned by R.D.I.C.C. and available only in 1994. A white ensign forms the handle.

NEPTUNE

Designed by Max Henk

D6548	Large	1961-1991
D6552	Small	1961-1991
D6555	Mini	1961-1991

Neptune was the Roman god of the sea. The symbol of his power was the trident he carried with which he could call forth, or subdue, storms. Neptune paying court to Amphritrite, came riding on a dolphin, seen here as forming a handle. He was more often seen riding the seas in a chariot drawn by horses with golden manes. It was said he created the horse, and he is also the patron of horse racing.

NORTH AMERICAN INDIAN

Designed by Max Henk

D6611	Large	1967-1991
D6614	Small	1967-1991
D6665	Mini	1981-1991

'Canadian Centennial Series 1867-1967'
Special backstamp 1967, when sold only in North America: See *Trapper* and *Lumberjack*.

Hiawatha rack plate Burslem 1908-1949

The 'Indian' race originally inhabited the whole of North America. Christopher Columbus, setting out from Europe to discover a sea route to the 'Indies' thought, on reaching the shores of America, he had achieved his goal, so the misnomer occurred. They were a handsome people, mainly nomadic, skilled hunters and having a culture with which the world has become familiarised mainly via Hollywood. Some early settlers, like William Penn, treated fairly with them, but, as the white man became greedy for more land, the red man was driven out of territories from Canada to Mexico, persecuted and subdued, so that the race declined.

Crested with great eagle feathers. –
Hiawatha (1855) Longfellow

89

OKOBOJI 75TH ANNIVERSARY

D6611   Large   1973

The Okoboji is a trap-shooting fraternity in the U.S.A. who adopt Indian names and dress and steep themselves in Indian lore. 'The chief' of the Okoboji presented 180 of these specially overprinted jugs at the annual 'pow-wow' in 1973.

D6786   Large   1987
New colourway commissioned by *John Sinclair*

OKOBOJI
75 ANNIVERSARY   **3**
1973

North American Indian
D6611
COPR 1964
DOULTON & CO LIMITED
Rd No 924806
Rd No 49145
Rd No 10602
Rd No 54/66

OLD CHARLEY

Designed by Charles Noke

D5420	Large	1934-1983
D5527	Small	1935-1983
D6046	Mini	1939-1983
D6144	Tiny	1940-1960
D5844	Tobacco Jar	1937-1960
D5858	Musical Jug	1938-1939
D5599	Ash Tray	1936-1960
D5925	Ash Bowl	1939-1960
D6012	Sugar Bowl	1939-1960
D6017	Teapot	1939-1960
D6030	Toby Jug-Large	1939-1960
D6069	Toby Jug-Small	1939-1960
D6110	Wall Pocket	1940-1960
D6152	Toothpick Holder	1940-1960
D5527	Table Lighter	1959-1973

See – *Higbee* for New colourway.

Sometimes an error in numbering on Small size character jug occurs. Referred to as 'Old Charlie' in some Collectors books.

Old Charley is a watchman. *'Charlies'* were created in the reign of Charles II (1660-1685) and named for him. They carried a bell, staff and lantern, and patrolled the streets, calling out the hour and *All's well* to reassure the citizens. The watchman was replaced in 1829 by the *Peeler*, the creation of Robert Peel and the precursor of the modern policemen.

90

OLD KING COLE

Designed by Harry Fenton

D6036	Large	1939-1960
D6037	Small	1939-1960
D6871	Tiny	1990
D6014	Musical Jug	1939

The tiny is a *R.D.I.C.C.* issue.

As in many other nursery rhymes, this character is based on a personage from history, in this case an early British ruler, but the jug clearly pictures the 'merry old soul' of the jingle.

Old King Cole was a merry old soul,
And a merry old soul was he;
He called for his pipe, he called for his bowl,
And he called for his fiddlers three.

OLD KING COLE

With yellow crown is the early version.

Found dated 1938. It was issued until mid 1939. It is from a different mould which is shown clearly in the ruff.

OLD KING COLE

Lambeth character jug probably by Leslie Harradine c.1910. A forerunner of the Burslem version this stoneware jug has a green crown and a pale green and beige overall glaze. It is only just over four inches high. It is outside the scope of the character jug collector, who is concerned with the range Charles Noke established at Burslem in 1934.

OLD SALT

Designed by Garry Sharpe

D6551	Large	1961-
D6554	Small	1969-

Designed by Peter Gee

D6557	Mini	1984-1991
D6782	Large	1987-1990

New Colourway

The mermaid's arm was modified in the miniature size soon after issue and became modelled in one with the body obviously for added strength.

Every quayside tavern in the world has its Old Salt, who spins endless yarns of exploits at sea, of mermaids and sea monsters. If plied with ale, the waves will break over the bar counter, on demand, until closing time!

PADDY

Designed by Harry Fenton

D5753	Large	1937-1960
D5768	Small	1937-1960
D6042	Mini	1939-1960
D6145	Tiny	1940-1960
D5845	Tobacco Jar	1939-1942
D5887	Musical Jug	1938-c.1939
D5926	Ash Bowl	1938-1960
D6151	Toothpick Holder	1940-1960

Paddy is the familiar name for an Irishman and a diminitive of Patrick, the patron saint of Ireland. On Saint Patrick's Day, 17th March, it is traditional to wear the shamrock, a trefoil plant which St. Patrick used to illustrate the Trinity. Our Paddy on the jug has a green coat, traditional dress for this day.

SANCHO PANÇA

Designed by Geoff Blower

D6456	Large	1957-1983
D6461	Small	1957-1983
D6518	Mini	1960-1983

Early versions 1957-1959.

Backstamp includes *A servant to Don Quixote.*

Sancho Panza, from *Don Quixote* (1605) by Cervantes, was appointed as his squire by Don Quixote. Mounted on a donkey, here forming the handle, this rustic followed his master on his many adventures, adding his homely common sense comment to the over-romantic Don's imaginings.

PASCOE & CO. INC. 101 Almeria Ave., Coral Gables, Florida 33134, U.S.A

QUEEN VICTORIA

D6913   Small   1992

Commissioned in a Limited Edition of 1,500 Numbered.

PEARLY KING

Designed by Stan Taylor

D6760	Large	1987-1991
D6844	Small	1987-1991

PEARLY QUEEN

D6759	Large	1987-1991
D6843	Small	1987-1991

Handles Bow-bells and pearl buttons.

Named for the pearl buttons with which they decorate their dress clothes, the Pearly King and Queen are both hereditary and elected holders of the office whose main duties are to raise money for charity.

Henry Croft was the first one to sew pearl buttons on his suit and collect for charity over 100 years ago. However, the *pearlies* have their roots as the elected spokespeople of the street market costers who needed solidarity against harassment by the police. These colourful characters can be seen at all the major London events from the Easter Parade to the Lord Mayor's Show, entertaining the crowd and rattling their collecting boxes.

JOHN PEEL

Designed by Harry Fenton

D5612	Large	1936-1960
D5731	Small	1937-1960
D6130	Mini	1940-1960
D6259	Tiny	1947-1960

John Peel (1772-1854) – famous huntsman immortalised forever by the song:

Contemporary portrait by J.H. Smith

D'ye ken John Peel with coat so grey?
D'ye ken John Peel at the break of day?
D'ye ken John Peel when he's far, far-away
With his hounds and his horn in the morning?

John Graves (1795-1885)

For forty years he hunted with a pack of hounds on the fells of Cumbria in North West England. The slopes were too steep for horses, and the hunt was often carried out on foot. John Peel wore a coat of local cloth in *Skiddaw* Grey making the red coat of the jug an error. He was a keen drinking man and at each kill the hunting party would adjourn to the nearest hostelry to celebrate.

Early models have the title on the reverse picked out in yellow.

THE PENDLE WITCH

Designed by Stan Taylor
D6826   Large   1989

Limited edition of 5,000.

Originally conceived and commissioned by *My Fair Lady*, a china retail firm in Lancashire, the character is a personification of a seventeenth-century legend of witch hunting. The project was abandoned and the design taken up by *Kevin Francis Ceramics*.

TOBY PHILPOTTS

Designed by Charles Noke

D5736	Large	1937-1969
D5737	Small	1937-1969
D6043	Mini	1939-1969

Toby Fillpot, as his name suggests, represents the archetypal toper, 'an habitual drinker of alcoholic liquors'. Toby was possibly derived from the French word *tope*, 'I pledge you' a toast. He is always represented as a merry fellow with a rosy complexion.

Toby Fillpot, a thirsty old soul,
As e'er drank a bottle or fathom'd a bowl.
In boozing about 'twas his praise to excell,
And among jolly topers he bore off the bell.
The Brown Jug, 1761.

MR. PICKWICK

Designed by Charles Noke and with later models by Harry Fenton

D6060	Large	1940-1960
D5839	Mid Size	1938-1948
D5839	Small	1948-1960
D6254	Mini	1947-1960
D6260	Tiny	1947-1960
HN1623	Bookend	1934-c.1939
M57	Napkin Ring	c.1935-c.1939
D6049	Bust	1939-1960
D6261	Small Toby Jug	1948-1960
D5839	Table Lighter	1958-1961

The small size was adapted by Harry Fenton with the handle at the back and different features.

Mr. Pickwick from *The Pickwick Papers* by Charles Dickens. Samuel Pickwick, a genial, kindly person, was Founder Member and President of the Pickwick Club. Created in the cause of scientific and cultural matters, it becomes the vehicle for a series of amusing adventures entered into by its members.

The eloquent Pickwick, with one hand gracefully concealed behind his coat-tails, the other waving in the air, to assist his glowing declamation.

MR. PICKWICK
SECOND VERSION

Designed by Bill Harper
D6959   Large   1994
Commissioned by *Lawleys by Post*.
In a Limited edition of 2,500.

This is the first jug with metal accessories –
the spectacles. The figural handle represents
Sam Weller, Pickwick's faithful servant.

PICK-KWIK WINES & SPIRITS

5 Derby Street, Burton-on Trent, Staffordshire.
All small size character jugs (c. 4 in) with
some adapted as flasks. 1982-1987.

LIMITED EDITIONS (2000 made)	1982
1. Mr. Pickwick No.1 (Pick-Kwik)	
2. Sgt. Buz Fuz (Dewars)	
3. Mr. Pickwick No.2 (Jim Beam)	
COLLECTORS' EDITION (1000 Made)	1984
4. Mr. Pickwick (Beam)	
5. Mr. Pickwick (Beam Black)	
LIQUOR CONTAINERS (2000 made)	
6. Mr. Micawber (Dewars)	
7. Mr. Micawber (Pkwk Deluxe)	1983
8. Sam Weller/Mr. Pickwick	
9. Old Mr. Turveydrop	1985
10. Town Crier of Eatanswill	1986
11. Uncle Sam (eagle)	
12. Uncle Sam (bottle)	1984
13. John Bull	
14. Capt.Cook	1985
15. Samurai Warrior	1986
(500 made)	1986
16. Uncle Sam ('In God We Trust')	
character jug (100 made)	1985

17. Mr. Micawber (Dewars) coloured jug.
18. Mr. Micawber (Pkwk Deluxe) coloured jug.
19. Mr. Micawber (Dewars) white jug.
20. Mr. Micawber (Pkwk Deluxe) white jug.
21. Mr. Micawber (Pkwk Deluxe) white liquor container.
22. Mr. Pickwick (PickKwik) white.
23. Sgt. Buz Fuz (no labels) white.
24. Sgt. Buz Fuz (Dewars) white with red transfers.
25. Mr. Pickwick (Jim Beam) white with red transfers.

PIED PIPER

Designed by Geoff Blower
D6403	Large	1954-1981
D6462	Small	1957-1981
D6514	Mini	1960-1981

The Pied Piper of Hamelin is a poem by Robert Browning based on an old legend from a town in Brunswick. The town is overrun by rats, the Mayor and corporation engage a stranger to rid them of the vermin. This he does by playing his pipe so sweetly that the rats follow the music and drown in the River Weser. His fee of one thousand guilders is unpaid, so the strange piper plays again, but this time all the children of the town follow him and disappear for ever.

A modeller very rarely gets it right first time and the studio is the place for experimentation. Geoff Blower tells of his *Pied Piper* jug with the single rat on the handle, that it was seen to be too 'mouse-like'. The pack of rats on the final jug are certainly more menacing.

A PILGRIM FATHER

Designed by David Biggs
D	Large	1969

A proposed jug to celebrate the 350th anniversary of the sailing of the *Mayflower* which forms its handle. It was probably found to be too expensive to produce.

THE PIPER

Designed by Stan Taylor
D6918   Large   1992
Limited edition of 2,500
Individually numbered.

I am indebted to collector Martin Coates for pointing out that Doulton has used a combination of details for this Scottish piper. The inclusion of lapel *Tiger badges* and sash badges indicate the piper is of the Gordon Highlanders. However the Gordon piper wears a bottle green tunic and a *Glengarry* cap. The red tunic is that of the Gordon drummers and as the character carries a white leather strap (which would support the drum) Doulton have created a combination character of Gordon piper/drummer, stating that the jug was *inspired by the famous Gordon Highlanders*. The red tunic of the drummer was probably chosen for it's popularity over the green and the imposing *bonnet* over a *Glengarry* cap.

Pipers traditionally led the Scottish regiments into battle. The bagpipes giving them heart and scaring the enemy. Once played in England, bagpipes are first mentioned in Scotland in the early fifteenth century and are now considered as Scotland's national instrument; they form the handle.

POACHER

Designed by Max Henk

D6429	Large	1955-
D6464	Small	1957-
D6515	Mini	1960-1991
D6464	Liqueur Flask	c.1960
D6464	Table Lighter	1958-1973
D6783	Large	1987-1989

New colourway

To poach is 'to trespass and capture game or fish in an illicit or unsportsmanlike manner'. In earlier times a starving man could be hanged for poaching the salmon that forms the handle of this jug, or worse, be transported to Australia for life!

PRESIDENTIAL SERIES

1. ABRAHAM LINCOLN

D6936   Large   1992
Limited edition of 2,500

2. THOMAS JEFFERSON

D6943   Large   1994
Limited edition of 2,500.

Other U.S. Presidents already included in the character jug range are Benjamin Franklin, Ronald Reagan, George Washington, Dwight Eisenhower and Theodor Roosevelt at Lambeth. (left)

PRISON OFFICER

A small size character jug proposed around 1991 which never got beyond the modelling stage. Similar in style to the *Journey through Britain* series, it was intended as a fund raiser by the *Latchmere House, Charity Fund*, Richmond Surrey.

PUNCH AND JUDY

Designed by Stan Taylor
D6946   Large   1994

Commissioned by the *R.D.I.C.C.* In an edition of 2,500.

A double sided elaborate jug with Punch and dog Toby on the face and Judy and the crocodile on the reverse with a string of sausages uniting them. Some of the elements of this traditional seaside show.

PUNCH AND JUDY MAN

Designed by David Biggs

D6590	Large	1964-1969
D6593	Small	1964-1969
D6596	Mini	1964-1969

The Punch and Judy man, of ancient origin, appeared in England at the end of the seventeenth century. He enacts a story of multi-murder, even to that of Toby the dog.

The hangman, the devil, a coffin and the gallows form part of the violent scenario, making it a popular diversion for children to this day. George Tinworth, at the Doulton Lambeth factory, modelled his charming mouse group in the 1880s, complete with small mouse peeping under the cloth at the back to see how the Punch and Judy man effects his magic.

QUAKER OATS LIMITED
London England.
MR. QUAKER

Designed by Harry Sales
Modelled by Graham Tongue

D6738   Large   1985

Printed on base: *Specially commissioned in celebration of the Company's 85th year.*

A limited edition of 3,500 each numbered and with certificate signed by Sir Richard Bailey, C.B.E. and Michael Doulton – this last a new departure. The jugs were for the company's internal use and for issue to *R.D.I.C.C.* members.

Mr. Quaker became the first registered trade mark of any breakfast food when he was chosen as a representative logo over 100 years ago. The character with his good natured appearance, personified purity, wholesomeness and integrity. The roots of the Quaker Oats Company can be traced to Scotland where oats had formed a staple food for many centuries. Two founding members were of Scottish descent, they formed a partnership and set up their first mill in Cedar Rapids, Iowa, U.S.A. in 1879. From there the company expanded to become a worldwide organisation. Quaker Oats became one of the most widely distributed products in the world and Mr. Quaker was instantly recognised wherever he appeared. The English Company was formed in 1899 and this jug commemorates that.

D.6738

MR QUAKER ®

Specially Commissioned
from
Royal Doulton ®
by
© QUAKER OATS LIMITED 1984

in celebration of the
Company's 85th year

Hand modelled & Hand Painted

Designed by HARRY SALES

Modelled by John G Tongue

A LIMITED EDITION of 3,500
of which this is no 29

DON QUIXOTE

Designed by Geoff Blower

D6455	Large	1957-1991
D6460	Small	1957-1991
D6511	Mini	1960-1991

Don Quixote by Cervantes was published in 1605, and is a burlesque on the romances of chivalry. Don Quixote is a poor gentleman of La Mancha in Spain. An amiable character, he imagines himself called upon to roam the world in search of adventure on his old horse, Rosinante, accompanied by his rustic squire, Sancho Panza. ('Quixotic' has come to describe the condition when the heart rules the head).

THE RED QUEEN

Designed by Bill Harper
D6777 Large 1987-1991
D6859 Small 1990-1991
D6860 Mini   1990-1991

The title is one of those surprising Doulton anomalies. *The Adventures in Wonderland* is associated with a pack of cards, *Through the Looking Glass,* a chess game. The Red Queen is a chess piece from the second book but this jug represents the Queen of Hearts from Wonderland. She carries her suit, a heart, on the axe which forms the handle of the jug. She so enjoyed having her executioner use it on any who displeased her, '*off with his* (or her or its) *head* ' was never far from her lips.

REGENCY BEAU

Designed by David Biggs
D6559 Large 1962-1967
D6562 Small 1962-1967
D6565 Mini   1962-1967

A Regency beau formed part of high society 'the ton', during the regency (1811-1820) of the later George IV. Their estates provided them with the money and leisure to make the tying of their cravats in the latest style the most important matter of their day. Leaders of fashion, such as Beau Brummel and the Prince Regent himself, were aped by the beaux. Quizzing glasses, walking canes, embroidered waistcoats and tasselled boots and, equally, the equipage of their 'high stepping' mounts were of far more importance than the Napoleonic or Anglo-American wars of the time.

REPUBLICAN NATIONAL COMMITTEE
RONALD REAGAN

D6718   Large   1984
*The President's signature edition, 1984
Presidential Election* with the President's
signature. Designed by Eric Griffiths under the
direction of the President's daughter, Maureen
Reagan. A limited edition of 2,000 each
numbered with a certificate and photograph of
the President in a decorative folio.

This jug was specially commissioned by the
Republican National Committee and is
available only through The Dallas Collection,
Nashua, N.H., U.S.A.

A major portion of the proceeds of this jug will
go to the James S. Brady Presidential Foundation. On 24th July 1984 No.1 of the edition
was presented to President Reagan at the White House by the President of the Royal Doulton
Company in the U.S.A., Paul M. Warner. No. 2 in the edition was presented by President
Reagan to James Brady, his Press Secretary, injured at the attempted assassination of the
President in 1981. The foundation's Charter authorises it to provide assistance to individuals
like Mr. Brady who are injured during similar tragedies in the future.

Ronald Reagan 1911-
His early career as a film actor in the 1940s brought him popular acclaim. He entered
politics becoming a most successful Governor of California in the 1970s. He became
President of the United States of America in 1981. An astute politician with a natural
charm and keen sense of humour, he has the ability to convince others of his enthusiasms.
His great charisma won him a second term of office in 1984. A few copies exist
commemorating the fiftieth inauguration in 1985.

RINGMASTER

Designed by Stan Taylor
D6863   Large   1991-1993
Pre-released by *The British Toby*.

The Ringmaster officiates at a circus performance.
He is usually portrayed as a magnificent but stern
authoritarian figure. This one however has a kindly
expression. He obviously attended the circus party
given in Toronto to launch this jug when a good time
was had by all. The *Maple leaf* backstamp celebrated
twenty-five years since the inauguration of Canada's
national flag.

One of the four *Circus Performers* introduced 1989-90.

ROYAL DOULTON INTERNATIONAL COLLECTORS' CLUB

Club Headquarters & U.K. branch
Minton House, London Road,
Stoke-on-Trent, ST4 7QD.

The Royal Doulton International Collectors Club was formed in 1980 and now has thousands of members worldwide. They receive a magazine each quarter *Gallery* on general topics of interest to collectors, plus advance news of new character jug releases. The club has its own special issues available to members only. All club issues have a special club backstamp. The club also acquires for members allocations of other large special issues, from world-wide promoters. There is a *For Sale* and *Wanted* supplement to the magazine of interest to collectors.

Michael Doulton is Honorary President of the Club and travels the world meeting club members. There are collectors club branches in Canada, the United States, Australia, New Zealand and South Africa and Collectors Club centres operate in many retail stores.

Sir Henry Doulton D6703

SPECIAL CLUB ISSUES

John Doulton D6656	1990-
Small Character Jug	
Sir Henry Doulton D6703	1984
Small Character Jug	
Pride and Joy HN2945	1984
Figure with Character Jug	
Albert Sagger D6745	1986
Doutonville Toby	
Auctioneer HN2988	1986
Figure with character jug	
Beefeater D6806	1988
Tiny character jug	
Old Salt D6818	1988
Figural teapot	
Old King Cole D6871	1990
Tiny character jug	
Charles Dickens D6901	1991
Small character jug	
Christopher Columbus D6911	1992
Small character jug	
King Edward VII D6923	1993
Small character jug	
Earl Mountbatten D6944	1993
Large Character jug	
Punch and Judy D6946	1994
Large character jug	
Nelson D6963	1994
Small character jug	

"Paddy."

RᵈNº817032.

Old Salt Teapot with Beefeater & Old King Cole Tinies

SALT RIVER CEMENT WORKS
U.S.A.

JOHN BARLEYCORN
D5327   Large   c.1939

PADDY
D5854   Tobacco Jar   1939
Both have special backstamps.

The above items appeared in a Phillips sale in 1986 before the collectability of backstamps had filtered through to dealers and auctioneers. The *John Barleycorn* jug was catalogued without mention of the backstamp and sold for a modest £70. I have assumed the SALT RIVER CEMENT WORKS are a U.S. firm where there are three rivers (at least) of that name, in Arizona, Kentucky and Missouri. Could a keen local collector, discover exactly where?

This overprinting, similar to the *Bentalls, Colemans* and *Darley* examples, seems to be a pre-war practice.

SCARAMOUCHE
Designed by Max Henk
D6558   Large   1961-1967
D6561   Small   1962-1967
D6565   Mini   1962-1967

Scaramouche was originally a character in the *Commedia dell 'arte,* and was always played as a cowardly and foolish boaster, dressed in the black costume of the Spanish Don. This version owes more to the colourful, swashbucking character played by Ramon Novarro in a film of 1923, and Stewart Grainger in 1952. Both films are adaptions of Sabatini's costume romance set in eighteenth-century France.

D6774 and D6814

SCARAMOUCHE
SECOND VERSION
D6814   Large   1988-1991

Here the black suit has been abandoned for a more colourful effect. The handle shows masks of comedy and tragedy relating him to the theatre.

D6774   Large   1987
A pre-release by *The Guild of Specialist China and Glass Retailers* in a new colourway. Limited edition of 1,500. Special backstamp.

SCARLET PIMPERNEL

A prototype designed by Geoff Blower, in the 1960's which was never put into production.

The Scarlet Pimpernel was the pseudonym of Sir Percy Blakeney, the hero of a romantic novel, *The Scarlet Pimpernel* by Baroness Orczy (1905) who in daring disguises rescued victims of the French *terror*.

SEAWAY CHINA CO.,

102 Broadway, Marine City, MI 48-039, U.S.A.

An exclusively Doulton store picturesquely situated on the southern shore of the Great Lakes and on the U.S.A./Canadian border.

SANTA CLAUS

Remodelled by Bill Harper

| D6950 | Tiny | 1993 | Plain handle |
| D6980 | Tiny | 1994 | Candy cane handle. |

Limited editions of 2,500. Special backstamp.

106

THE SHAKESPEARE COLLECTION

This collection was issued at a higher price than that of the general range Large size jugs. This marked a new departure and the trend continues. In 1994 there are eight different prices for large size jugs in the General Range. Prestigious issues can add even more and higher prices.

WILLIAM SHAKESPEARE

Designed by Michael Abberley
D6689   Large   1983-1991

William Shakespeare (1564-1616) was born and died at Stratford-on-Avon in Warwickshire. He married Anne Hathaway in 1582, left Stratford about 1585 and journeyed to London where he entered the theatre as a player. He became a playwright and wrote the many masterpieces known and enjoyed all over the world. The quill forming the handle of this jug rests in an ink pot in the form of the *Globe Theatre,* on the South Bank of the Thames, where many of his plays were first performed and which is being rebuilt at the present time.

© ROYAL DOULTON TABLEWARE LIMITED 1982
D 6671

The
Shakespearean
Collection
HENRY V
A series of hand-made, hand-decorated Character Jugs by Royal Doulton

HAMLET

Designed by Michael Abberley
D6672   Large   1982-1989

Hamlet is a Prince of Denmark. On his father's death he is supplanted by his uncle who marries the dead king's widow with indecent haste. His father's ghost appears and tells of his murder, and calls upon Hamlet to avenge him. As the play proceeds the wicked uncle is eliminated, but so also is Hamlet, along with most of the leading characters in this famous tragedy.

Goodnight sweet prince and flights of angels sing thee to thy rest!

OTHELLO

Designed by Michael Abberley
D6673   Large   1982-1989

In Othello (1604) Shakespeare tells the story
of a Moor who became a successful general in
the service of the Venetian State. He also wins
the love and hand in marriage of the beautiful
Desdemona. His success breeds envy. The
handle is formed by Iago, a soldier whose
promotion Othello has overlooked.
He instigates a plot to convince Othello that
his wife has been unfaithful to him. In a
passion of jealously Othello murders her, but
on discovering her innocence is so remorseful
that he kills himself.

O! beware, my Lord of jealousy;
It is the green eyed monster which doth mock
The meat it feeds on.

ROMEO

Designed by David Biggs
D6670   Large   1983-1989

Romeo is a Montague, one of the two chief
families of Verona, whose story is told in
Romeo and Juliet (1597). He falls in love with
Juliet who is a Capulet, the sworn enemies of
the Montagues. Juliet returns his love and
they are secretly married, but their love cannot
overcome the enmity of the two families. It is
only when the final tragedy of the deaths of
Romeo and Juliet is discovered that the
enemies are at last reconciled. The handle is
here formed as the balcony on which Romeo
climbed to woo his Juliet.

But soft, what light through yonder
window breaks?
It is the east and Juliet is the sun.

HENRY V

Designed by Robert Tabbenor
D6671   1982-1989

Henry V (1413-1422) first appears as Prince
Hal in Shakespeare's *Henry VI,* a youthful
merrymaking figure who spends his time
making mischief and roistering with Falstaff
and his fellows in taverns. When he comes to
the throne, at the age of 26, he turns his back
on his former friends and settles down to the
serious business of being king. He is victorious
at Agincourt (1415) against the French.
Fighting a gallant battle against great odds,
he rouses his men with inspiring speeches.
He marries the French princess, Katherine, to
cement the relationship of the two countries,
and becomes heir to the throne of France.
The handle is formed by Henry's royal
standard which is a combination of the arms
of England and France.

Once more into the breach,
dear friends, once more.

MACBETH

Designed by Michael Abberley
D6667   Large   1982-1989

Basing his play loosely on an incident in
Scottish history, Shakespeare tells of two
generals, Macbeth and Banquo, who meet the
three witches forming the handle of this jug.

The witches foretell that Macbeth will become
King of Scotland, but that Banquo's heirs will
inherit the kingdom. Macbeth becomes king
and, aided by a scheming wife, he does all he
can to prevent the prophesy coming true even
to murdering Banquo. However, when the
curtain falls, both Macbeth and Lady Macbeth,
with many more characters, have died violent
deaths, and all the predictions of the witches,
however improbable, have been fulfiled.

There's dagers in men's smiles

WILLIAM SHAKESPEARE

Designed by Bill Harper
D6933   Large   1993-

A limited edition of 2,500.

A double handled prestigious loving cup with six of the writer's characters modelled on the handles, *Hamlet, Falstaff* and *Titania* on the left and *Romeo, Juliet* and *Touchstone* on the right. Original selling price £250 as opposed to the following which was £35.

WILLIAM SHAKESPEARE

Designed by Bill Harper
D6935   Small   1993

© ROYAL DOULTON TABLEWARE LIMITED 1982
D 6871

The
Shakespearean
Collection
HENRY V
A series of hand-made, hand-decorated Character Jugs by
Royal Doulton

Macbeth prototype

110

BILL SHANKLY

Designed by Bill Harper
D6914   Small 3.5in   1992

A special commission to commemorate *The Liverpool Football Club* centenary. A Limited edition of 5,500 available from *L.F.C.* Numbered.

Bill Shankly 1918-1981 was *Liverpool Football Club's* most famous manager. The handle shows the Club's crest and two footballs.

Some people think football is a matter of life and death... I don't like that attitude. I can assure them it is much more serious than that.
                                        Bill Shankly 1973.

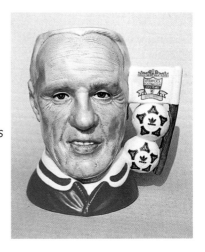

TAM O'SHANTER

Designed by Max Henk
D6632   Large   1973-1980
D6636   Small   1973-1980
D6640   Mini   1973-1980

A Kingsware flask for Greenlees Tam O'Shanter 7 in Burslem 1911

Tam O'Shanter – a poem by Robert Burns (1790). It tells of a farmer, Tam o'Shanter, returning home one night well primed with liquor, coming upon the Devil with attendant witches, he is observed and chased by one of the witches, and flees to safety over the Bridge of Doon, losing only his grey mare's tail, which was all that remained in the witches' territory. The handle shows the witch holding the tail.

111

JOHN SHORTER

Designed by Bill Harper
D6880   Small   1991

Limited edition of 1,500.
Special backstamp, numbered.

Commissioned by *The Character and Toby Jug Collectors Society of Australia* to commemorate their tenth anniversary. It being the first collectors club to commission their own jug.

Figural handle is a kangaroo.

A prototype was produced with a blue bow tie but a maroon one was the final choice.

No.1 was presented to Mr. John Shorter their Patron.

John Shorter C.B.E., whose family has been closely connected with Royal Doulton, as Australian retailers, since his grandfather founded the business; started work for the firm in 1929 in the packing department at one pound a week. In 1930 he spent six months in England working in various potteries, but mainly Doulton's, gaining experiences of the trade. He has returned to Staffordshire at intervals since. He knew Charles Noke and his son Cecil, Cuthbert Bailey and many other famous Doulton names. His travels included the Lambeth and other Doulton factories and the world. In 1947 he travelled to England by flying boat – the journey taking nine days each way.

In 1956 he became Chairman and Managing Director of his company and retired from it in 1971 when Doulton bought out the firm to do their own distribution in Australia. The next year, John Shorter opened his own china and glass retail shop in Sydney. In 1977 he was awarded the C.B.E. for services to the British Export Trade. Of course behind every successful man is a talented woman and Mr. and Mrs. Shorter have already celebrated their Diamond wedding. Now past 80 and having handed on some of the responsibility of the firm to his son and daughter, he is full of unquenchable energy, charm and is a mine of information on all things Doulton which he is always eager to pass on.

THE CHARACTER AND TOBY JUG COLLECTORS SOCIETY OF AUSTRALIA,

P.O. Box R94, Royal Exchange, Sydney, N.S.W. 2000, Australia.

Patron – John Shorter
President – Dan Downie

The Society is not only fortunate in its Patron but in its officers. It celebrates its fifteenth anniversary in 1995 and is as active as ever. It meets every month in Sydney and produces an informative newsletter, to which many world-wide collectors subscribe.

SIMON THE CELLARER

Designed by Charles Nokes and Harry Fenton

D5504	Large	1935-1960
D5616	Small	1936-1960
D6956	Tiny	1994

Simon the Cellarer was immortalised in a nineteenth-century drinking song. The handle is formed from the keys to his cellars which were full of the fine wines in his care, of which he was a connoisseur.

Old Simon the Cellarer
keeps a rare store of Malmsey
and Malvoisie, and Cyprus,
and who can say how many more,
for a chary old soul is he,
Of Sack and Canary he never doth fail,
And all the year round
there is a brewing of ale.

W.H. Bellamy

SIMPLE SIMON

Designed by Geoff Blower

D6374	Large	1953-1960

Simple Simon – a character in a nursery rhyme of that name. It tells of the exploits of a silly, gullible fellow, and ends:

He went for water in a sieve,
But soon it all ran through.
And now poor Simple Simon
Bids you all adieu.

JOHN SINCLAIR
266 Glossop Road, Sheffield,
S10 2MS China and Glass.

GOLFER
D6784   Large   1987
RIP VAN WINKLE
D6785   Large   1987
NORTH AMERICAN INDIAN
D6786   Large   1987
Limited edition of 1,000 each. New
colourways of current jugs with special backstamps.

JOHN LENNON

D6797   Mid size 5in   1988
Numbered edition of 1,000. New colourway with an on-glaze red uniform

LITTLE MESTER

D6819   Large   1988
A numbered edition of 3,500.

This character bears the local name given to
the craftsmen in the cutlery trade at Sheffield,
which has been associated with it for 600
years. The handle of the jug is composed of a
bowie knife and a grinding wheel. Stan Taylor
modelled this jug on Roland Swinden, blade
grinder and finisher. A bowie knife made by
him was presented to the Sir Henry Doulton
Museum. To commemorate the fact that knives
were made at Sheffield for Alamo hero Jim
Bowie, who gave them his name, a *Little
Mester* jug was presented to the Alamo, San Antonio,
Texas, in July 1988. Legend has it that a bowie knife
carrying the mark of George Wostenholm, a Sheffield
cutler, was found on the body of Jim Bowie after the
Battle of the Alamo (1836).

SHEFFIELD WEDNESDAY
D6958   Small   1993
A football supporter jug.

Probably the most impressive launching ceremony for any
character jug was given by JOHN SINCLAIR on 23rd June
1988 at the magnificent Cutlers Hall in the presence of
the Master Cutler, the Lord Mayors of Sheffield and
Stoke-on-Trent, the local Member of Parliament, Royal
Doulton executives and 350 other distinguished and
privileged guests connected with Sheffield or the Doulton
world. The Royal Doulton Band played in the gallery
during the banquet and a very good time was had by all.

114

THE SITE OF THE GREEN, Dundas, Ontario, Canada L9H 5EI

Retail store which has commissioned:

LEPRECHAUN

D6847   Large   1990
D6899   Small   1991

The Site of the Green shamrock logo and boxed. Limited edition of 500 each.
Both jugs entered the general range the following year. In Canada the small size 4in is
known as medium and the miniature as small, which leads to some confusion.

SLEUTH

Designed by Alan Moore
D6631   Large   1973-
D6635   Small   1973-
D6639   Mini   1973-1991

As with the Royal Doulton figurine *The
Detective* (HN2359) introduced in 1977,
this jug is based on the character of Sherlock
Holmes, created by Sir Arthur Conan Doyle
(1859-1930). They both show the
deerstalker hat, the pipe and magnifying
glass sported by this first of the great
fictional detectives. However, in the 1970s
copyright to the name was still held by Sir
Arthur Conan Doyle's executors. It must have
been with great celebration that Doulton
issued a commemorative toby of 'fifty years
since the author's death' when copyright had
ceased. (see D6661 *Sherlock Holmes Toby*)

SLEUTH

D6773   Small   1987
Commissioned by *Lawleys by Post*
In a limited edition of 5,000 to
commemorate the centenary of *A Study in
Scarlet* Sherlock Holmes' first story.
New colourway with red coat.

SMUGGLER

Designed by David Biggs
D6616   Large   1968-1981
D6619   Small   1968-1981

The inn was a favourite haunt of the smuggler, and probably much of his booty could be found in its cellars. Many old inns have secret escape passages, so that the excise officers could not surprise the smugglers drinking with their friend, the landlord.

Five and twenty ponies trotting through the dark. Brandy for the parson, 'baccy for the clerk;
Rudyard Kipling.

SMUTS

Designed by Harry Fenton
D6198   Large   1942-c. 1948

Printed on the base: 'Field Marshall The Rt.Hon. J.C. Smuts, K.G., C.H., D.T.D., Prime Minister of the Union of South Africa and Commander-in-Chief South African Forces.'

Jan Smuts (1870-1950) – statesman, soldier and philosopher. A great South African who enjoyed a unique reputation throughout the world. Of Dutch descent and a farmer's son, he studied law in England. In the Boer War he fought against the British, but was a valued ally in the two world wars. He was a member of the Unionist Cabinet in 1910, and was twice Prime Minister of South Africa in 1919-24 and 1939-48. He played an important part in the formation of the League of Nations and the United Nations, and tried to promote racial harmony in South Africa.

On the handle is a springbok, a gazelle which is South Africa's national emblem.

On sale in South Africa in 1942 where 1/- was donated for every jug sold to *Mrs. Smuts' Comforts Fund* for the South African troops. *In great demand although circumstances made supplies difficult.*

SNAKE CHARMER

Designed by Stan Taylor
D6912   Large   1991
Limited edition of 2,500.
Exclusive to the U.S.A.
Launched at Collectors Club Conference at
Higbees, Cleveland. On 15 November 1991.
Special numbered backstamp. Same design
number as *The Bahamas Policeman*.
This is a very colourful character and exotic
looking jug, showing a grey-bearded snake
charmer in a bright yellow turban. The handle
is formed by a cobra, its basket and the flute
used to *charm* it. The snake rises out of the
basket and sways to the music seemingly in a
trance. A sight you are bound to see, as I have,
if you visit India, but its secret is not divulged.

SNOOKER PLAYER

Designed by Stan Taylor
D6879   Small   1991-1994

One of a series of eight sporting subjects.
Issued in the small size only in 1990-1991.
Handle composed of cue, snooker balls and
chalk.

Snooker has a great following in the U.K.
especially since it has translated so well to the
T.V. screen. The game has derived from the
game of billiards but it is played with twenty
two balls which have different scoring values.
The maximum possible score, *break*, at one
turn is 147. World champions like Steve Davis
and Stephen Hendry dominate the game for a
time but there is always the possibility of a
new rising star replacing them.

SNOWMAN

Designed by Martyn Alcock
D6972   Mini   1994
U.S.A. exclusive

ANTONY & CLEOPATRA

Designed by Michael Abberley
D6738   Large   1985-1991
A limited edition of 9,500. The first of a series of four jugs. Printed on the base the special
Star-crossed lovers' backstamp. 'Star-Crossed Lovers' is a quote from Shakespeare's *Romeo and Juliet*.

Caesar Augustus sent Mark Antony to Egypt to consolidate his interests there. Antony on
meeting the Queen of Egypt was so enthralled with her beauty that he forgot his allegiance
to Rome. The lovers opposed Caesar and were defeated. They met their deaths by their own
hand – he by the sword and she by the asp, which form the handle.
The story of these lovers has been told many times, by Plutarch, Shakespeare, Dryden and
De Mille. Cleopatra's legendary beauty has been personified in modern times by Elizabeth
Taylor playing opposite Richard Burton's Antony.
Finish, good lady; the bright day is done, and we are for the dark.   Shakespeare.

NAPOLEON & JOSEPHINE

Designed by Michael Abberley
D6750   Large   1986-1993

Napoleon occupies the front of the
jug. In the other three the lady takes
precedence. Born in Martinique
(1763), Josephine, at sixteen
married a French nobleman who
was guillotined during the
revolution. At thirty-three she
married Napoleon. Captivated by her liveliness and beauty he wrote her passionate love
letters from his many campaigns. They became Emperor and Empress of France in 1804.
However, as with many other great rulers he needed an heir to consolidate his power. He
divorced Josephine in 1809 to marry the daughter of the Emperor of Austria. She gave him
the wanted son. Josephine died in 1814 a year before Napoleon met his defeat at Waterloo.
Here Josephine wears the roses in her hair, for which her house at Malmaison was famous
and the handle has her mirror and fan backed by the *Tricolore*.
I send you a thousand kisses. I am in bed.   Bonaparte to Josephine, 1797.

118

SAMSON & DELILAH

Designed by Stan Taylor
D6787　Large　1988-1993

Samson, a Nazarene had great strength. When only a youth he killed a lion with his hands, the lion, whose head forms the spout of this jug. He is also said to have killed a 1,000 Philistines with the jawbone of an ass and this forms the handle of the jug. He fell in love with Delilah who was persuaded by his enemies, the lords of the Philistines, to find out the secret of his strength. Samson gave her three false answers but finally he told her the secret was in his hair which had never been cut. When he fell asleep in Delilah's lap she had him shaved and he was taken, blinded and imprisoned.

On a feast day he was paraded in the Philistine temple. His hair had grown and asking God's help he pulled down the column supports to which he was chained, also shown on the handle. He was killed together with all the assembled company. There is no mention of Delilah. I feel she lived on to enjoy her reward of silver.

Softly awakes my heart.

Samson et Dalila

KING ARTHUR & GUINEVERE

Designed by Stan Taylor
D6836　Large　1989-1993

The Arthurian legends have been written and embroided by many writers through the centuries. They tell of a young virtuous king whom with his sword *Excalibur* defeats many enemies and conquers many countries, bringing peace and prosperity to his people. He lives in *many-towered Camelot* and brings there his Queen Guinevere.

He creates a band of virtuous knights whose quest is the search for the Holy Grail. One of them, Lancelot, falls in love with Guinevere and she with him. They flee to Brittany, Lancelot's home. Arthur pursues them and is mortally wounded in the battle which ensues. The handle on this jug has Excalibur on one side and the Holy Grail on the other. This Guinevere has a look of Vanessa Redgrave who played her in the film *Camelot* 1967.

'Tis better to have loved and lost than never to have loved at all.

Tennyson.

STATUS QUO

Designed by Martyn Alcock

Francis Rossi	D6961	Small	1993
Rick Parfitt	D6962	Small	1993

Commissioned by *Fantom Music Co. Ltd.*
In a Limited edition of 2,500.

Status Quo, a successful pop duo whose
career in 1993 had spanned 28 years.
They had recorded 44 hit singles, more
than any other group, 22 of which hit the
top ten. They had completed 20 world tours. Performed for *Live Aid* at Knebworth.
Performed for Royalty and are immortalised at Madame Tussauds and now as Doulton
character jugs.

CITY OF STOKE-ON-TRENT
Jubilee Year, 1959-1960

Stoke-on Trent is the world's largest
ceramic centre and was formed in 1910
from Burslem, Hanley, Longton, Stoke-on-
Trent, Fenton and Tunstall. Almost all
character jugs are made at the Beswick
factory, Longton, and guided tours take
place daily (0782 291210).

TO COMMEMORATE THE
300'S ANNIVERSARY
OF THE
"COMPLEAT ANGLER"
1653 - 1953

CITY OF
STOKE-ON-TRENT
"IZAAK WALTON
D. 6404
OFR 1953
DOULTON & CO LIMITED
R:N: 671560
R:N: 31604
R:N: 6825
R:N: 237/53
JUBILEE YEAR
1959-1960
WITH THE COMPLIMENTS OF
LORD MAYOR AND LADY MAYORESS
ALDERMAN HAROLD CLOWES O.B.E. J.P.
AND
MISS CHRISTINE CLOWES

Various contemporary large size character
jugs overprinted. *With the compliments of
Lord Mayor and Lady Mayoress Alderman Harold Clowes, O.B.E., J.P. and Miss Christine
Clowes. Izaak Walton, Bacchus* and *Viking* have appeared and there are more. It is thought
about sixty or seventy of each could have been supplied.

STRAWBRIDGE & CLOTHIER
(Department Store) Philadelphia, U.S.A.

SAIREY GAMP	D6770	Large	1986

Limited edition of 250
To commemorate the opening of the Doulton Room in
November. A new colourway of a discontinued jug
with a yellow bow and hat trim.

SAIREY GAMP	D6789	Small	1987

Limited edition of 500
To commemorate the first anniversary of the opening
a small size version of the same colourway was sold.

CHELSEA PENSIONER

D6833   Large   1988
Limited edition of 250 to celebrate the second anniversary of the Doulton Room. A new design by Stan Taylor which entered the general range in January 1989. Also issued to *Higbee, Horne* and *Holmes* under their own backstamps.

ELEPHANT TRAINER

D6841   Large   1989
Limited edition of 250 to celebrated the third anniversary of the Doulton Room. Also issued to *Higbee, Horne* and *Holmes*. Special backstamps. A pre-release.

BASEBALL PLAYER
Philadelphia Phillies

D6957   Small   November 1993
Limited edition of 300 to celebrate 125th anniversary. Special colourway of red cap and red striped uniform.

TOUCHSTONE

Designed by Charles Noke
D5613   Large   1936-1960

Touchstone is the clown in Shakespeare's *As you Like It.* He accompanied Celia and Rosalind in their exile in the Forest of Arden. 'He is a mixture of the ancient cynic philosopher with the modern buffoon, and turns folly into wit, and wit into folly, just as the fit takes him.' William Hazlitt.

All the world's a stage, and all the men and women merely players:
As you Like It – Shakespeare

TOWN CRIER

Designed by David Biggs

D6530	Large	1960-1973
D6537	Small	1960-1973
D6544	Mini	1960-1973
D6920	Small Toby	1992-1993

Before the days of cheap printing, when newspapers made news available to all, the town crier was the means of spreading information. He first rang his bell to attract a crowd and cried. 'Oyez!, Oyez!, which is Norman French for 'Hear Ye!', and then read his proclamation, which, together with his bell, forms the handle of this jug.

TOWN CRIER
SECOND VERSION

Designed by Stan Taylor
D6895   Large   1991-

Doulton include this in their *London Collection* but he belongs in smaller cities and towns. In London they proclaim with heralds and great pomp and circumstance.

THE TRAPPER

Designed by Max Henk and David Biggs

D6609	Large	1967-1983
D6612	Small	1967-1983
D	Mini	1983

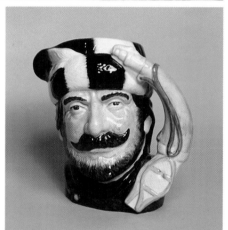

A miniature size was made and appears on the market from time to time. They are not as rare as reported.

Special backstamp in 1967, when sold only in North America:
'Canadian Centennial Series 1867-1967'.
  (See *Lumberjack* and *North American Indian*).

Here is another tough and hardy character from North America's early history – the trapper of animals for their skins. The snow-shoes on the handle suggest the rigours of weather with which the trapper had to contend. However, it was a lucrative occupation, and the flourishing trade in furs was responsible for much of the 'opening up' of the North American Continent.

PIERRE TRUDEAU

A large prototype exists. Commissioned by *The British Toby* but release of copyright could not be obtained to put the jug into production.

Pierre Elliot Trudeau   1919-

A French Canadian from Quebec, by profession a lawyer, he rose to become Minister of Justice and Attorney General at 48 in 1967. Elected Liberal Party Leader he became Prime Minister of Canada in 1968. He promoted economic and diplomatic independence for Canada. He lost support by 1984 and resigned.

FRIAR TUCK

Designed by Harry Fenton
D6321   Large   1951-1960

Friar Tuck was a legendary friar who joined
Robin Hood's band of outlaws in the oak
forests of Sherwood. A fat, jovial character,
very fond of his food and drink, and yet,
despite his rotund figure, a brave and good
fighter. He appears in various adaptations of
the story including Scott's *Ivanhoe* (1819) and
the many cinema versions of *Robin Hood*.
In the definitive 1938 film version the part
was perfectly taken by the many-chinned
Eugene Pallette.

DICK TURPIN

Designed by Charles Noke & Harry Fenton

D5485	Large	1935-1960
D5618	Small	1936-1960
D6128	Mini	1940-1960
D6953	Tiny	1992
D5601	Ashtray	1936-1960

Dick Turpin (1706-1739) – an infamous
highwayman who was finally arrested for horse
stealing and hanged at York. Legend has
transformed him into a romantic figure, dashing
through the night on his horse 'Black Bess',
shown as a handle in the second version.
Sometimes has the initials R.T. on the handle
of the pistol in the first version.

DICK TURPIN
SECOND VERSION

Designed by David Biggs (with mask)

D6528	Large	1960-1981
D6535	Small	1960-1981
D6542	Mini	1960-1981

MARK TWAIN

Designed by Eric Griffiths

D6654	Large	1980-1990
D6694	Small	1983-1990
D6758	Mini	1986-1990

Small size exclusive to Walt Disney's EPCOT Center in Orlando, Florida, during 1982

Mark Twain was the pen-name of Samuel Clemens 1835-1910, American writer and wit. He was born in Missouri and was at one time a pilot on the Mississippi, and so adopted the call of the leadsman, sounding the passage down the river, as his pseudonym. Although he travelled to, and wrote of, other countries and other subjects the books he is best remembered for are those telling the adventures of Tom Sawyer and of Huckleberry Finn, both epics of the Mississippi.

The report of my death was an exaggeration.
  Cable from Europe to the Associated Press

UGLY DUCHESS

Designed by Max Henk

D6599	Large	1965-1973
D6603	Small	1965-1973
D6607	Mini	1965-1973

This jug was based on the original *Alice* illustrations by Sir John Tenniel 1820-1914

This character is from *Alice's Adventures in Wonderland (1805)* by Lewis Carroll.

The Duchess, who was 'very ugly', and Alice were invited by the Queen of Hearts to play croquet. The mallets were flamingoes (one forms the handle of this jug) and the balls were hedgehogs. As one was twisting about whilst the other was running away, tempers were frayed. An added peril was that if any player broke the rules of the game they were likely to be sentenced by the Queen, who shouted the order to her soldiers 'Off with her head".

U.K. FAIRS LTD.
Nick Tzimas, Doug Pinchin, Ipswich, Suffolk, U.K.

FALSTAFF

D6795   Large   1987   Limited edition of 1,500

An attractive new colourway of a current jug with mustard collar and feather to celebrate the fifth Annual Doulton Collectors Fair held on 25th October 1987 at the Park Lane Hotel, Piccadilly. (see page 43)

U.K. INTERNATIONAL CERAMICS
10 Wilford Bridge Spur, Melton, Woobridge, Suffolk IP12 IRJ, U.K.

THE GREAT GENERALS
DUKE OF WELLINGTON

Designed by Eric Griffiths,
Modelled by Bill Harper
D6848   Large   1989
Limited edition of 3,500

Arthur Wellesley, Duke of Wellington 1769-1852. British Soldier and Statesman was knighted for his Army service in India. He was an outstanding Commander in the Peninsular War and expelled the French from Spain in 1814. He finally defeated Napoleon at Waterloo in 1815. He was Tory Prime Minister from 1828-30 and Foreign Secretary 1834-5.

Backstamp quotes 5,000 as edition but only 2,500 were made.

GENERAL GORDON

Designed by Bill Harper
D6869   Large   1991
Limited edition of 1,500

Charles George Gordon (1833-1885) Joined the Army at 16 and served as a Lieutenant in the Crimea War, 1855. He was posted to China at 30 and commanding the Chinese Army he suppressed the Taiping Rebellion, 1859-65 and acquired the name *Chinese Gordon*. Later in his career he served in India and the Sudan. He gained the reputation of being arrogant, ruthless, fearless, forthright and opinionated. He was also high spirited, witty and popular with his peers.

When at home in Gravesend he was charitable and caring and worked to improve the lot of the poor, especially children. He ran a free school at his home in the evenings and is remembered by a Doulton statue of him by John Broad in Gordon Park, Gravesend. Appointed Governor of the Sudan in 1873-9 and again in 1884 when he was sent to rescue the Egyptian Garrisons under attack by the Mahdi's Army in Khartoum; he was killed there two days before the relieving force arrived.

GENERAL EISENHOWER

Designed by Bill Harper
D6937   Large   1993

Limited edition of 1,000
To commemorate the 50th anniversary of the U.S. landings in North Africa.

General Dwight D. Eisenhower (1953-1961) was a prominent military leader. He was Commander in Chief of Allied Forces on the invasion of Continental Europe in the Second World War. He resigned from the Army in 1947 to become President of Columbia University, write his memoirs and play golf. A popular figure known affectionately as *Ike* he was not-too-reluctantly pressured into running for President of the U. S. He beat the intellectual Adlai Stevenson by 442 votes to 89 and served as President from 1953-1961. Three of *Ike's* commands are shown on the backstamp.

U.K. International Ceramics have negotiated the copyright release to produce an Elvis Presley character jug scheduled for 1995.

GENERAL PATON   **1994**
GENERAL MACARTHUR   **1995**

VETERAN MOTORIST

Designed by David Biggs
D6633   Large   1973-1983
D6637   Small   1973-1983
D6641   Mini   1973-1983

This character is probably a present-day owner
of a veteran car, dressed in the style of his
grandfather, about to compete in the veteran
car commemorative run. The 'old crocks' all of
pre-1905 vintage, make the run from Hyde
Park in London to Brighton each November,
marking the day in 1896 when an act was
passed in the British parliament making it no
longer necessary for a car to be preceded by a
man on foot waving a red flag to warn the
public of the approaching hazard. The motoring
age had begun.

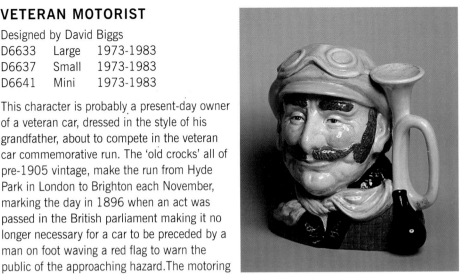

THE VICAR OF BRAY

Designed by Charles Noke and Harry Fenton
D5615   Large   1936-1960

Some copies of this jug have a very
pronounced yellow rim to the hat, until 1947
when it was remodelled.

'The Vicar of Bray' is the title of a traditional
song, based on the story of a vicar who was
twice a Roman Catholic and twice a Protestant
in the reigns of Henry VIII, Edward VI, Mary
and Elizabeth, a time of religious persecution.
He observed,

If I changed my religion...
I kept true to my principle,
which is to live and die the Vicar of Bray.

QUEEN VICTORIA

Designed by Stan Taylor
D6816   Large   1989-1991

D6913   Small   1992
commissioned by Pascoe & Co., Florida
U.S.A, in a limited edition of 1,500.
Numbered.

QUEEN VICTORIA

D6788   Large   1988

Commissioned by *The Guild of
Specialist China & Glass Retailers* in
a new colourway with a purple and
yellow crown etc.

Queen Victoria 1819-1901
Victoria became queen at the age of 18 in 1837 almost by default, as her father the Duke
of Kent, was the only one of George III's fifteen children who could produce a legitimate heir
to ensure the succession. The throne she inherited was even in danger of being
overwhelmed by the rising tide of revolution in Europe. However, in the '60 glorious years'
of her reign this small, unprepossessing woman saw the monarchy, England and the British
empire grow and prosper.

Much of its prosperity was engineered by the many brilliant entrepreneurs of the age; one of
whom was Sir Henry Doulton. When she died in 1901, Victoria was revered and loved as a
mother figure throughout a large part of the world.

She wrought her people lasting good.

Inscription on Lambeth Commemorative.

VIKING

Designed by Max Henk
D6496   Large   1959-1975
D6502   Small   1959-1975
D6526   Mini   1959-1975

The Vikings were Scandinavian adventurers
who, between the eighth and eleventh
centuries, sailed out in their skillfully built long
ships terrorising, plundering and settling most
of the known world from Russia to Greenland
and even some of the then unknown North
American continent. The handle of this jug is
formed by the dragon-carved prow of a Viking
long ship.

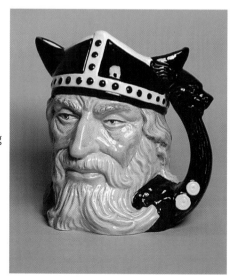

VILLAGE BLACKSMITH

The Village Blacksmith
Designed by Max Henk
D6549   Large   1961

A prototype not issued.

WALRUS AND CARPENTER

Designed by Max Henk
D6600   Large   1965-1980
D6604   Small   1965-1980
D6608   Mini   1965-1980

The Walrus and the Carpenter, in *Through the Looking Glass* 1871 by Lewis Carroll, invite four plump, young oysters for
A pleasant walk, a pleasant talk,
Along the briny beach

The last verse reads,
'O oysters,' said the Carpenter,
'You've had a pleasant run!
Shall we be trotting home again?'
But answer came there none -
And this was scarcely odd, because
They'd eaten every one

ISAAC WALTON

Designed by Geoff Blower
D6404   Large   1953-1982

Printed on the base:

'To celebrate the 300th anniversary of the publication of 'The Compleat Angler'.

Isaac Walton (1593-1683) – a writer of biographies who is remembered chiefly for his discourse on fish and fishing, *The Compleat Angler*, 1653. Geoff Blower based this jug on a portrait by Jacob Huysmans in the National Gallery, London.

*And when the timorous trout I wait to take,
and he devours my bait,
How poor a thing, sometimes I find,
will captivate a greedy mind.*

*Doulton Seriesware designs were inspired
by The Compleat Angler*

Lambeth plaque by John Broad 1906.

GEORGE WASHINGTON

Designed by Stan Taylor

D6669	Large	1982-
D6824	Small	1989-1991
D6825	Mini	1989-1991

Issued to commemorate the 150th anniversary of his birth. Available only in North America during 1982.

George Washington (1732-1799) was Commander-in-Chief of the revolutionary armies of the thirteen States of America who fought against the British for their independence, which was recognised in 1781.

His choice as first President of the United States was a foregone conclusion; he was the man whom the hour and the nation demanded. A trusted representative of the people, he served two terms (1789-1797) and refused a third. The capital city of the U.S.A. is named for him.
The handle of the jug is formed by the Declaration of Independence scroll.

GEORGE WASHINGTON

D6669	Large	1989
D6824	Small	1989

Special backstamp commemorating the 200th anniversary of the selection of the first President of the United States, for sale in the U.S.

SAM WELLER

Designed by Charles Noke with the later
models by Harry Fenton

D6064	Large	1940-1960
D5841	Mid Size	1938-1948
D6140	Small	1940-1960
D6147	Mini	1940-1960
D6147	Tiny	1940-1960
D6052	Bust	1939-1960
M61	Napkin Ring	c.1935-1939
D6265	Small Toby Jug	1948-1960

The small size jug was adapted by Harry
Fenton with the handle at the back and
different features.

Sam Weller, from *The Pickwick Papers* (1837) by Charles Dickens was the son of coachman
Tony Weller, and is first met as *Boots* at *The White Hart* inn. He becomes Mr. Pickwick's
valet and faithful aide. A typical Cockney, he is good natured, bright, sharp and able to
contrive a good scheme for anything.

A bright red handkerchief was wound in a very loose and unstudied style round his neck

TONY WELLER

Designed by Charles Noke with the later
models by Harry Fenton

D5531	Extra Large	1936-1942
D5531	Large	c.1945-1960
D5530	Small	1936-1960
D6044	Mini	1939-1960
HN1616	Bookend	1934-c.1939
D5888	Musical Jug	1937-c.1939
D6013	Sugar Bowl	1939-1960
D6016	Teapot	1939-1960
D6051	Bust	1939-1960
M60	Napkin Ring	1935-1939

Tony Weller – a character from *The Pickwick Papers* by Charles Dickens. A stage-coachman
and a widower, marries again 'an uncommon pleasant widder', but lives to regret his
imprudence and warns others. 'Beware of the widders'. His second wife obligingly dies and
leaves him to enjoy his single state, having inherited her pub, the 'Marquis of Granby'.

Then he would bury in a quart pot as much of his countenance
as the dimensions of the quart pot admitted of its receiving.

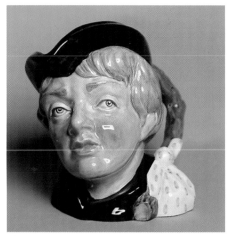

DICK WHITTINGTON

Designed by Geoff Blower
D6375   Large   1953-1960

Richard Whittington (c.1358-1423) is shown here as the poor boy of the pantomime story with all his possessions tied in a kerchief. He is in the act of running away because of ill treatment, but hears Bow Bells ringing out. 'Turn again Whittington, Lord Mayor of London'. He returns to the City and, with the help of his cat, finds success and fortune.

The Richard Whittington of history was born wealthy and achieved great wealth through trade (in French *achat:* perhaps the original of the story's cat). Kings were among his creditors. He was four times Mayor of London between 1397 and 1420, and became a great benefactor to the City, endowing its charities, libraries, colleges and churches, and providing a free water supply for the people.

DICK WHITTINGTON, LORD MAYOR OF LONDON

Designed by Bill Harper
D6846   Large   1989

Commissioned by *The Guild of Specialist China and Glass Retailers* in a Limited edition of 5,000. Special backstamp. Numbered.

Early portrait of Dick Whittington and cat

132

WILD WEST SERIES

D6711	**WYATT EARP**	Designed by Stan Taylor
D6731	**DOC HOLLIDAY**	Designed by Stan Taylor
D6732	**ANNIE OAKLEY**	Designed by Stan Taylor
D6733	**GERONIMO**	Designed by Stan Taylor
D6735	**BUFFALO BILL**	Designed by Robert Tabbenor
D6736	**WILD BILL HICKOCK**	Designed by Michael Abberley

A series of jugs in a mid size 5.5 in (14 cm) issued for sale in the U.S.A. in September 1985 and worldwide. 1986-1989.

GERONIMO (1834-1909) was thin lipped, hard eyed, cruel and a hater of the white men who had killed his wife and children. Geronimo was the last leader of the Apache Indians, and the Apaches the last of their race to be subdued. When Geronimo surrendered in 1886, the Apache country became Arizona, which with its mountains, Indians and painted desert is the perfect setting for the 'Wild West' of fiction. The country of **WYATT EARP** (1848-1929). Fresh from carving a gun fighting reputation as a Marshall in Dodge City he came to Tombstone, Arizona, accompanied by three of his gun fighting brothers, lured there by reports of rich silver strikes. They stayed to wage war on the outlaw element. The culmination was a gunfight at the O.K. Corral. With Earp at this showdown was his friend and ally **DOC HOLLIDAY** (1852-1887). John Henry Holliday was a lawyer's son who formerly had a dentistry practice in Baltimore. On being told at 20 that he was consumptive and to prolong his life he should seek a healthier climate and lead a temperate life, he moved west. He acquired great wizardry with firearms and the Bowie knife and soon began a career of gambling, brawls, killings and imprisonment. Always one step ahead of the law, 'Doc', lean sardonic and deadly, died in a sanatorium at the age of 35.

JAMES BUTLER HICKOCK – 'WILD BILL' (1837-1876) acted as army scout and spy for the Yankees in the Civil War. After the war he had many careers, U.S. Marshall, army scout, mail carrier, guide and sherriff, all interlaced with his particular brand of law keeping. In a saloon he once killed three men and wounded a fourth, all strangers, for drawing attention to his large nose and unkempt appearance. He met his own death in a saloon during a game of poker. He was a friend of Will Cody and appeared on the boards with him in some early theatricals.

WILLIAM FREDERICK CODY – BUFFALO BILL' (1845-1917) was one of eight children. He lost his father at eleven years old and in order to help out the family budget got a job carrying messages on horseback between the wagon trains of a freight line. Later he rode for the celebrated 'Pony Express' before the railways were built. He gained his name as a supplier of buffalo meat to men engaged in laying the railway lines. He killed 4,820 animals in eighteen months. He later formed 'Buffalo Bill's Wild West Show' and toured the United States and Europe.

ANNIE OAKLEY (1860-1926) appeared with Buffalo Bill's Show for seventeen years. She was a backwoods gal who through necessity became a crack shot. She broke a golden rule when she entered a marksmanship contest against Frank Butler and beat him. Irving Berlin based his popular musical *Annie Get your Gun,* on her story. Despite the words he gave her to sing 'You can't get a man with a gun' she did and became Mrs. Butler. They toured the halls together. Chief Sitting Bull, who appeared in Buffalo Bill's Show with Annie gave her the nickname 'Little Sure Shot'. She was adopted by the Sioux nation and was presented to Queen Victoria.

THE WILLIAMSBURG COLLECTION

Colonial Williamsburg is an ambitious historical restoration of an eighteenth-century town in the U.S.A. It was the capital of Virginia, the oldest of the British colonies in America and named in honour of King William III. It ceased to be the seat of government in 1780 and, losing its importance, fell into decline so that, as time passed, it kept much of its original character.

John D. Rockerfeller, Jnr., financed the original restoration of the town in 1926, and the work is carried on by the foundation he endowed. The homes, shops and taverns are given a natural 'lived in' look with authentic early English and American furnishings. George Mason, who travelled to Williamsburg in 1776, to deliver his Virginian Declaration of Rights, would feel quite at home in this eighteenth-century time capsule.

Hotels and restaurants are included in the complex to accommodate its many visitors. The town is peopled by hundreds of staff, dressed in costume, who carry on trades and live in eighteenth-century style.

Royal Doulton, in 1960, introduced seven Williamsburg personalities into the HN figurine range and, in 1963, the following seven characters were introduced into the character jug range and they remained in production for twenty years.

APOTHECARY

Designed by Max Henk

D6567	Large	1963-1983
D6564	Small	1963-1983
D6581	Mini	1963-1983

BLACKSMITH

Designed by David Biggs

D6571	Large	1963-1983
D6578	Small	1963-1983
D6585	Mini	1963-1983

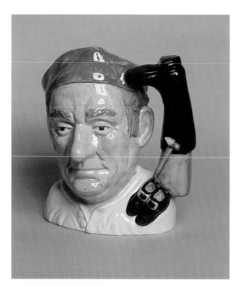

BOOTMAKER

Designed by David Biggs
D6572   Large   1963-1983
D6579   Small   1963-1983
D6586   Mini   1963-1983

GAOLER

Designed by David Biggs
D6570   Large   1963-1983
D6577   Small   1963-1983
D6584   Mini   1963-1983

GUARDSMAN

Designed by Max Henk
D6568   Large   1963-1983
D6575   Small   1963-1983
D6582   Mini   1963-1983

GUNSMITH

Designed by David Biggs
D6573   Large   1963-1983
D6580   Small   1963-1983
D6587   Mini   1963-1983

NIGHT WATCHMAN

Designed by Max Henk

D6569	Large	1963-1983
D6576	Small	1963-1983
D6583	Mini	1963-1983

CABINET MAKER

It was announced in the Royal Doulton Collectors Booklet of 1981 that this additional model was to be added to the Williamsburg range in that year. Although a prototype was modelled, it was not put into production as it was soon decided to discontinue the whole series.

RIP VAN WINKLE

Designed by Geoff Blower

D6438	Large	1955-1994
D6463	Small	1957-1994
D6517	Mini	1960-1991
D6463	Liqueur Flask	c. 1960
D6463	Table Lighter	1958
D6785	Large	1987

Rip van Winkle from *Sketch Book* (1819) by Washington Irving, who based his story on an earlier one told by Dutch settlers. The story tells of a man who, walking in the Catskill mountains, meets some strange little people. After drinking a *draught of Hollands*, he falls asleep, and sleeps for twenty years. When he returns to his village and finds all changed and *even his old dog has forgotten him*, he realises he drank a fairy potion.

Rip Van Winkle Seriesware rack plate Burslem 1907

New colourway commissioned by *John Sinclair*. Black Hat, Green Jacket and Handle

137

WITCH

Designed by Stan Taylor
D6893   Large   1991

Witch, a sorceress who uses her powers for either good or evil. In fact there are white and black witches. This one is in the guise of an ugly old woman would seem to be rather evil. She is shown with her familiar, a black cat. One of three *Mystical characters, the Witch* and *the Genie* had a production of only a year.

WIZARD

Designed by Stan Taylor
D6862   Large   1990-
D6909   Small   1992-

The Wizard is a magician and sorcerer with supernatural powers. A wizard can work for good or evil. The handle here shows a wand and a black cat. The only one of the three *Mystical characters* retained in the general range.

YACHTSMAN

Designed by David Bigs
D6622   Large   1971-1980

Small and miniature sizes were piloted.

Your author has enjoyed the pleasures of yachting, a definition of which has been given as 'standing in a cold shower, tearing up bank notes'. However, it is only the pleasures and the homecomings that one remembers, whether one is a 'Sunday sailor', a round-the-world yachtsman or woman, or a member of the Perth Yacht Club bringing home the America's Cup in 1983.

YACHTSMAN
SECOND VERSION

Designed by Stan Taylor
D6820   Large   1989-1991

Pre-released by *The Canadian Association of Art and Collectables Shows,* Durham, Ontario, Canada. At their first show in July 1988. Limited Edition of 750.
Special backstamp.

YEOMAN OF THE GUARD

Designed by Stan Taylor
D6873   Large   1991-1994

Issued as part of *The London Collection*

AN EPILOGUE

So I come to the last jug and the last character in the list. I have come to terms with Doulton labelling the Queen of Hearts, *The Red Queen* of their putting *John Peel* and *The Piper* in red coats, giving London a *Town Crier* and *Anne Boleyn* an axe.

I accept these anomalies as I do the comic rewriting of English history in North American publications, but whilst they are far away, Stoke-on-Trent is only 130 miles from London! The modeller knew what he was doing no doubt, they research their work very well, but somewhere someone in marketing decided 'red' sells and 'navy' doesn't, a ruff looks very nice and a decorated hat too so that who knows who our Yeoman is supposed to be? Is he a *Yeoman of the Guard,* as his title suggests? This is a body of men already mentioned in *Beefeater.* Founded by Henry VIII in 1485 to guard his person. In those days they served at the King's table as *Buffetiers,* hence the corruption *Beefeaters* another duty was to make the King's bed, to search it for bombs etc. before the Royal person got in. They now serve in a purely ceremonial role and attend the Queen on State occasions in their Tudor costume.

The Yeoman Warders of the Tower, on the other hand, are a much more ancient body, being formed in Norman times to guard the Tower of London, a Royal Palace, and a state prison. Three jugs have been produced, all wearing the red tunic and ruff of the Queen's bodyguard but ravens and keys belong only to the Yeoman Warders of the Tower. The ravens are all that remain of a menagerie kept at the Tower in former times and the legend says that when the ravens leave the disintegration of the Kingdom will take place. Therefore they are very well looked after by the Yeoman Warders.

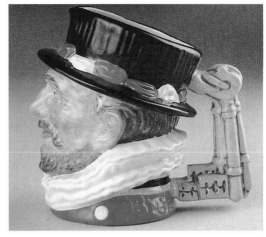

The oldest military ceremony in the world, *The Ceremony of the Keys* is performed by the Yeoman Warders every night. It is the formal locking up of the Tower in the name of the Queen. The prototype jug with the bunch of keys handle made in the 1980's was meant to record this.

The Yeoman Warders of the Tower are drawn from Warrant Officers with at least 22 years service in the Army, Air force or the Royal Marines, but not the Navy. They must hold a long service and good conduct medal with a recommendation from their Colonel. There was originally a height stipulation of 5' 10". They have their own accommodation in the Tower principally in a row of houses called *The Casemates.*

A thousand years of English history is disturbed with this jug so I've tried to redress things by being rather long winded but it is time the Yeoman Warders were recognised. One of them is a jug collector so we could have a good moan about the situation together. In England some things change very little in a thousand years but although always two distinct bodies of men they have recently been known to double their duties on State occasions and change costumes in these budget conscious times. The general public, knowing no better, do address them all as *Beefeaters*, but at least we know better don't we?

YEOMAN OF THE GUARD was pre-released in 1990 by:-
Dillards, of New Orleans, Louisiana, U.S.A. 50 jugs D6883
To commemorate the third anniversary of the opening of the Royal Doulton room.
Joseph Horne, Pittsburgh, Pennsylvania, U.S.A. 75 jugs. D6882
To commemorate the third anniversary of the opening of the Royal Doulton room.
Strawbridge & Clothier, Philadelphia, Pennsylvania, U.S.A. 75 jugs. D6885.
To commemorate the fourth anniversary of the opening of the Royal Doulton room.
Higbee, Cleveland, Ohio, U.S.A. 250 jugs. D6884
To commemorate the fifth anniversary of the opening of the Royal Doulton room.
I was only exasperated by the poor Yeoman Warder losing out but what about the poor jug collector hoping to obtain one of the 50 jugs with the *Dillard* backstamp and what would be the price? I would say to that collector, just don't bother, you can have two very similar looking *Beefeater and Yeoman of the Guard* jugs on your shelf without having four more Yeoman with different backstamps. As with all collecting, collect what you like and looks good in your home. I have had to record the printed backstamps here for you, but they don't always have a lot of artistic merit and they can quite well remain on the pages.

TOBIES

CHARLIE

Designer unknown. Large 11 in. (28 cm.) 1919
With removable 'bowler' and 'CHARLIE' inscribed on
the base.

GEORGE ROBEY

Designer unknown
Large 10 5 in 26.5cm. 1925

A commissioned toby with removable 'bowler'. Traditionally, early tobies were lidded.
George Robey inscribed on base. The example shown here is dated 1926.

George Robey (1869-1954) was the son of a civil engineer and was educated at Dresden,
Leipzig and Cambridge before entering his father's profession. It was as a successful
amateur that he got his first chance on the stage, and his success was immediate and
continuous. He became a great star of the British music hall and later appeared in
pantomime and revue. His one venture into Shakespeare, as Falstaff, was a triumph. He

was billed as *The Prime Minister of Mirth* and his trade marks were
his heavy eyebrows, and rather battered appearance, topped by a
bowler hat. He delighted millions, but always remained a rather
aloof and lonely figure above the footlights. He was knighted, like
Chaplin, rather belatedly at the end of a long life and career.

He played Tony Weller in the film of *Pickwick Papers* made in
1952 when he was 83.

A Self Caricuature

OLD CHARLEY
Designed by Harry Fenton
D6030   Large 9 in
D6069   Small 5.5 in
          1939-1960

HAPPY JOHN
Designed by Harry Fenton
D6031   Large 9 in
D6069   Small 5.5 in
          1939-1991

FALSTAFF
Designed by Charles Noke
D6062   Large 9 in
D6063   Small 5.25 in
          1939-1991

TOBY XX
Designed by Harry Fenton
D6088   6.5 in   1939-1969

THE BEST IS NOT TOO GOOD
Designed by Harry Fenton
D6107   4.5 in   1939-1960

HONEST MEASURE
Designed by Harry Fenton
D6108   4.5 in   1939-1991

JOLLY TOBY

Designed by Harry Fenton
D6109   Medium 6.5 in
          1939-1991

WINSTON CHURCHILL

Designed by Harry Fenton
D61271 Large 9 in
D6172   Medium 5.5 in
D6175   Small 4 in 1941-1991

THE HUNTSMAN

Designed by Harry Fenton
D6320   Large 7.5 in
          1950-1991

THE SQUIRE

Designed by Harry Fenton
D6319   Medium 6 in
          1950-1969

SIR FRANCIS DRAKE

Designed by M. Abberley
D6660   Large 9 in
          1981-1991

SHERLOCK HOLMES

Designed by R. Tabbenor
D6661   Large 8.75 in
          1981-1991

SMALL SEATED DICKENS TOBIES

Designed by Harry Fenton

D6261	Mr. Pickwick	1948-1960
D6262	Mr. Micawber	1948-1960
D6263	Sairey Gamp	1948-1960
D6264	Fat Boy	1948-1960
D6265	Sam Weller	1948-1960
D6266	Cap'n Cuttle	1948-1960

All are 4.5 in high, and the names are incised on the base.

JOHN WESLEY

Charles Noke designed a toby jug as John Wesley in the traditional Staffordshire style in the early 1920s. When the prototype was produced Noke began to have misgivings about the propriety of producing a likeness of this good man and abstainer in a shape associated with strong drink. It was decided to shelve the project and what was thought to be the only copy was given to its painter, Ted Eley. However an Australian collector spotted another copy in the museum of the Wesley Church, Tasmania. Presented by a Mr. Harris who is said to have had a hand in the design in 1932. There could be others. The base is inscribed 'John Wesley M.A. born 1703 died 1791. Founder of Methodism'. On one side 'The world is my parish' and on the other 'A brand plucked from the fire.' The handle is a flaming brand referring to his rescue from Epworth Rectory fire.

The mark dates it between 1923-27.

John Wesley 1703-91
Founder of the Evangelic movement of Methodism. He took gospels to the masses, touring Britain on horseback, preaching in the open air to whoever would listen. The movement has now spread worldwide.

I took upon all the world as my parish

Journal 1789

All toby jugs were withdrawn at the end of 1991. In 1992 a new set of small tobies was begun.

JESTER

Designed by Stan Taylor
D6910 Small 5" 1992-1993
Limited Edition of 2,500

TOWN CRIER

Designed by Stan Taylor
D6920 Small 1992-1993
Limited Edition of 2,500

CLOWN

Designed by Stan Taylor
D6935 Small 1993-
Limited Edition of 3,000

KING & QUEEN OF DIAMONDS 1994

Designed by Stan Taylor
D6969 Small 1994
Limited Edition of 2,500

FATHER CHRISTMAS

Designed by Bill Harper
D6940 Small 1993-
Limited Edition of 3,500

Special backstamp and
certificate.

LEPRECHAUN

Designed by Stan Taylor
D6948 Small 1994-
Limited Edition of 2,500

This is an authentic
Leprechaun, a fairy
shoemaker with a pot of
gold, no rainbow but lucky
shamrocks.

KING & QUEEN OF CLUBS 1995

A proposed set of four
double-sided tobies
illustrating the King and
Queen of the suits.

D6699	MR. LITIGATE,	Lawyer	1983-1991
D6700	MISS NOSTRUM,	Nurse	1983-1991
D6701	MR. FURROW,	Farmer	1983-1989
D6702	REV. CASSOCK,	Clergyman	1983-1991
D6713	MR. TONSIL,	Town Crier	1984-1992
D6714	MADAME CRYSTAL,	Clairvoyant	1984-1989
D6715	MRS. LOAN,	Librarian	1984-1990
D6716	BETTY BITTERS,	Barmaid	1984-1991
D6720	SERGEANT PEELER,	Policeman	1985-1992
D6721	CAPTAIN SALT,	Sea Captain	1985-1992
D6722	MISS STUDIOUS,	Schoolmistress	1985-1989
D6723	DR. PULSE,	Physician	1985-1992
D6740	MAJOR GREEN,	Golfer	1986-1992
D6741	MIKE MINERAL,	Miner	1986-1990
D6742	FRED FLY,	Fisherman	1986-1992
D6743	MR. BRISKET,	Butcher	1986-1992
D6766	ALDERMAN MACE,	Lord Mayor	1987-1992
D6767	FLORA FUCHSIA,	Florist	1987-1990
D6768	CHARLIE CHEER,	Clown	1987-1992
D6769	MONSIEUR CHASSEUR,	Chef	1989-1992
D6809	FRED FEARLESS,	Fireman	1989-1992
D6811	LEN LIFEBELT,	lifeboatman	1989-1992
D6812	CAPTAIN PROP,	Pilot	1989-1992
D6813	PAT PARCEL,	Postman	1989-1991

THE DOULTONVILLE TOBIES

Doultonville is the creation of William Harper, who was born, has studied and worked in the Potteries all his life. In this town of his imagination live the 'larger-than-life' characters whom Bill has created as small size toby jugs 4 in.

This range was first issued in 1983, and other inhabitants were added until 1989. We can read of the adventures of the Doultonville characters in the charming stories written by Bill.

First three discontinued in 1989. All were discontinued in 1991-2.

D6745 Albert Saggar, Potter 1986, see R.D.I.C.C.

PROMOTIONAL TOBY JUGS & FLASKS

ASPREY & CO.LTD. (Jewellers)
New Bond Street, London W1

Designed by Harry Fenton 9.5 in.
1920-c. 1930

Two figural whisky decanters with detachable heads. One modelled as a Scotsman to contain Scotch whisky, and the other an Irishman to contain Irish whiskey.

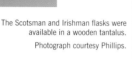

The Scotsman and Irishman flasks were available in a wooden tantalus.
Photograph courtesy Phillips.

CHARRINGTON & CO.LTD. (Brewers)
Mile End, London

Toby   Large 9.25 in.   c.1934-1938
There are three versions, the bases being inscribed thus:
1. *TOBY ALE* (311) c. 1934
2. *ONE TOBY LEADS TO ANOTHER*
3. *CHARRINGTON'S*   1938

Trade mark registered in 1907 by *Hoare*.

Hoare & Co., Ltd. were taken over by Charrington in 1933. The jug is based on the *Toby* trademark, first used by Hoare's and in use by Charrington until the present day. Other firms produced similar Toby jugs in this Charrington copyrighted design.

148

CLEVELAND FLUX CO.
Ohio, U.S.A.
CLIFF CORNELL

A full seated toby commissioned in 1956.

Large 9"	Brown suit	500 copies
Large 9"	Brown suit	500 copies
Large 9"	Beige suit	unknown
Medium 5.5"	Blue suit	375 copies
Medium 5.5"	Brown suit	375 copies
Medium 5.5"	Beige suit	unknown

A small size prototype was submitted c. 2.25 in.
Printed on the base *Greetings Cliff Cornell 'Famous
Cornell Fluxes' Cleveland Flux Company.*

Examples exist with colour variations especially in details such as the tie.

Cliff Cornell was an Ohio industrialist who commissioned jugs in his own likeness from the
Doulton factory for distribution to friends and business associates. The similarity between

these and the Churchill tobies is not
accidental as, reputedly, Mr. Cornell
was an admirer of Winston Churchill.

The jugs were sent at Thanksgiving
with a greeting card saying that Cliff
Cornel, was sorry he couldn't be with
you but place it on your table and the
jug would carry his greeting.

149

WILLIAM GRANT & SONS LTD.

Glenfiddich Distillery, Banffshire, Scotland
Designed by Graham Tongue.
Character jug as decanter representing the founder,
William Grant.

WILLIAM GRANT

Large Decanter 1986. Four oak casks handle.
Edition of 500 to mark the centenary of the founding
of the firm in 1886.

WILLIAM GRANT

Large Decanter 1987. Four oak casks handle.
Edition of 2,500 'To celebrate 100 years since the
first whisky flowed from the stills'.

WILLIAM GRANT

Large Decanter 1988. Field officer's sword handle.
Edition of 5,000.

All jugs filled
with Grant's
twenty-five year
old Scotch
whisky. Special
backstamps.

William Grant

Founder of William Grant & Sons Ltd
An independent family company for five generations
Specially Commissioned from
Royal Doulton ®
Hand Modelled and Hand Painted
Designed and Modelled by: *Tongue*
Grant's 25 Year Old Very Rare Scotch Whisky
Specially filled in 1987, celebrating the 100 years since
the first whisky flowed from the stills of William Grant's
Highland Distillery.
100 YEARS OF ACHIEVEMENT
Blended and Bottled by
William Grant & Sons Ltd
The Glenfiddich Distillery, Banffshire, Scotland
Product of Scotland
750ml 43% vol.

W. WALKLATE LTD. (BOTTLERS)

D6385	FALSTAFF	c. 1956
D6463	RIP VAN WINKLE	c. 1956
D6464	POACHER	c. 1956

Three small size character jugs adapted as
flasks were commissioned to contain BOLS
peach brandy, etc. They were sealed with a
cork and a paper label with a further paper
label at the neck. *Rip van Winkle* is the rarest.

See *Pickwick Collection*

DERIVATIVES
ASH TRAYS 3"

D5599	OLD CHARLEY	1936-1960
D5600	PARSON BROWN	1936-1960
D5601	DICK TURPIN	1936-1960
D5602	JOHN BARLEYCORN	1936-1960

ASH BOWLS 3"

D5925	OLD CHARLEY	1938-1960
D5926	PADDY	1938-1960
D6006	AULD MAC	1939-1960
D6007	FARMER JOHN	1939-1960
D6009	PARSON BROWN	1939-1960
D6009	SAIREY GAMP	1939-1960

BOOKENDS

Busts about 4" high, mounted on wooden bases.

HN1615	MR. MICAWBER	1934-c.1939
HN1616	TONY WELLER	1934-c.1939
HN1623	MR. PICKWICK	1934-c.1939
HN1625	SAIREY GAMP	1934-c.1939

Catalogue page showing two bookends and two tobacco jars available in 1938.

BUSTS

D6047	SAIREY GAMP	1939-1960
D6048	BUZ FUZ	1939-1960
D6049	MR. PICKWICK	1939-1960
D6050	MR. MICAWBER	1939-1960
D6051	TONY WELLER	1939-1960
D6052	SAM WELLER	1939-1960

MUSICAL JUGS

D5858   OLD CHARLEY   1937-1942
'Here's a Health unto His Majesty'

D5887   PADDY   1938-1942
'An Irish Jig'

D5888   TONY WELLER   1938-1942
'Come, Landlord Fill the Flowing Bowl'

D5889   AULD MAC   1938-1942
'The Campbells are Coming'

D6014   OLD KING COLE   1939-1942
'Old King Cole'
Yellow version exists.

These musical jugs are fitted with a 'Thorens' Swiss movement. Production was interrupted by the outbreak of war, and musical jugs were probably not made long after its commencement. This is borne out by the rarity of *Old King Cole*.

The title of the melody is printed around the base.

MUSICAL JUGS

NAPKIN RINGS

M57	MR. PICKWICK	c.1936-c.1939
M58	MR. MICAWBER	c.1936-c.1939
M59	FAT BOY	c.1936-c.1939
M60	TONY WELLER	c.1936-c.1939
M61	SAM WELLER	c.1936-c.1939
M62	SAIREY GAMP	c.1936-c.1939

SUGAR BOWLS 2.5" 6.5cm

D.6011	SAIREY GAMP	1939
D6012	OLD CHARLEY	1939
D6013	TONY WELLER	1939

Gift suggestions
from *Modern Home*
Christmas 1936

Catalogue page of ten table lighters available in 1958

TABLE LIGHTERS 3.5"

D5838	BUZ FUZ	1938
D5842	CAP'N CUTTLE	1958
D5843	MR. MICAWBER	1958
D6453	PORTHOS	1958
D6463	RIP VAN WINKLE	1958
D6233	BEEFEATER	1958-1973
D6385	FALSTAFF	1958-1973
D6386	LONG JOHN SILVER	1958-1973
D6464	POACHER	1958-1973
D5839	MR. PICKWICK	1958-1961
D5527	OLD CHARLEY	1959-1973
D6504	LAWYER	1962-1974
D6505	BACCHUS	1964-1974
D6506	CAPTAIN AHAB	1964-1974

The above characters were adapted by Doulton to house cigarette lighters. The rarest subjects are those made in 1958 only. Previously, the *van Cleff Studios*, New York. U.S.A. had adapted some small character jugs for this purpose by filling them with plaster of Paris.

TEAPOTS

D6015	SAIREY GAMP	1939
D6016	TONY WELLER	1939
D6017	OLD CHARLEY	1939

A contemporary catalogue illustration showing the three teapots with their matching sugar bowls and cream jugs available in the U.S.A. in 1939

TEAPOTS

A new set of figural teapots was introduced in 1988 with the *R.D.I.C.C* offer of *Old Salt*. Three more soon followed in the general range but were all discontinued in 1991 making them almost as rare as the previous set to future collectors.

OLD SALT R.D.I.C.C.	D6818	1988
LONG JOHN SILVER	D6853	1989-1991
FALSTAFF	D6854	1989-1991
OLD BALLOON SELLER	D6855	1990-1991

All were modelled by Bill Harper

TINIES 1.25"

Issued between 1940 and 1960

D6142	FAT BOY	1940-1960
D6143	MR. MICAWBER	1940-1960
D6144	OLD CHARLEY	1940-1960
D6145	PADDY	1940-1960
D6146	SAIREY GAMP	1940-1960
D6147	SAM WELLER	1940-1960
D6255	'ARRY	1947-1960
D6256	'ARRIET	1947-1960
D6257	AULD MAC	1947-1960
D6258	CARDINAL	1947-1960
D6259	JOHN PEEL	1947-1960
D6260	MR. PICKWICK	1947-1960

Note that the Second World War hindered the completion of this set. Most of the rare derivatives, it can be seen, were issued around the outbreak of the Second World War and were probably not produced long after its commencement.

The title occurs on the base of the first six issued in 1940 only.

See also *Dickens Tinies and Diamond Collection.*

TOBACCO JARS 5.5"

| D5844 | OLD CHARLEY | 1938-1942 |
| D5854 | PADDY | 1939-1942 |

156

TOOTHPICK HOLDERS 2.25"

D6150	SAIREY GAMP	1940-
D6151	PADDY	1940-
D6152	OLD CHARLEY	1940

WALL VASES 7.25"

D6110	OLD CHARLEY	1940-1941
D6111	JESTER	1940-1941

SPECIAL GIFT BOXES

Containing two miniature jugs were sold in the 1950s.

The three combinations available were:
1. Old Charlie and Sairey Gamp
2. Mr Pickwick and Mr Micawber
3. John Peel and Beefeater

A leaflet was enclosed picturing some popular jugs and informing the recipient that there were 'over fifty subjects for your choice', so obviously it was expected that the gift would encourage new collectors.

The spelling of *Charlie* above is taken from the leaflet.

COLLECTORS NOTES
ARTISTS
LESLIE HARRADINE 1902-1912

Designed some character jugs at Lambeth about
1910. They were all in salt-glaze stoneware but
with various finishes. They included *Pecksniff* 7 in,
ivory and treacle glaze; *A Highwayman* 6.5 in
brown salt glaze with added darker glaze; *Old King
Cole* 4.25 in ivory with added green colour;
Theodore Roosevelt 5.5 in brown salt glaze.
Harradine left the Lambeth studios in 1912 to
work freelance. He went to Canada but returned to
take part in the First World War. Invalided out he
spent the rest of his life in warm climates, Majorca,
Spain and the Channel Islands. From there he sent

figurine models, but no character jugs, to Burslem by post for a further 45 years.

HARRY SIMEON 1896-1936

Designed a range of toby jugs at Lambeth c. 1925 which obviously influenced some of the
Burslem range introduced in 1939. He studied modelling and sculpture at Huddersfield
School of Art and won a scholarship to the Royal College of Art. From there he went to
Doulton and produced many hand-painted plaques and vases but he excelled in modelling.
His simplistic style was well suited to the many slip-cast productions he introduced
including his *Toby Wares*.

CHARLES NOKE 1889-1941

Art Director at Burslem from 1914-1936 he introduced the character and toby jug range
we know and collect today in 1934. He modelled many of the earliest jugs, such as *John
Barleycorn, Parson Brown.* Shared his love of jesters with *Jester* and his love of Charles
Dickens when he modelled the six Dickens characters. *Simon the Cellarer* and *Dick Turpin*
were done in collaboration with Harry Fenton. *Mephistopheles* and *Cardinal* were
developments of his early vellum figures.

HARRY FENTON 1903-1911 AND 1928-1953

Was Head of the Modelling Shop and worked closely with Charles Noke. Geoff Blower
paints a wonderful picture of him 'he was a bachelor, small and quick, he wore gold, oval
specs and a flat cloth cap which he never took off. He had a long purplish nose which
invariably had a 'dewdrop' on it, and constantly smoked a pipe filled with herbal tobacco'.
In the 1920's he worked in the U.S.A. for 10 years and his speech was peppered with
Americanisms. The faces of many of his jugs had a textured 'scumbled' effect. *Friar Tuck,
Sam Johnson, Johnny Appleseed.*

MAX HENK 1949-1973

Max's great grandfather came from Germany to work at Mintons. The whole family had a
tradition of fine painting and modelling. Max started in tableware but was directed to work
on character jugs in his spare time. This was a usual practice! He was a fine modeller and

the first to make the handle an added feature. He was fond of characters from literature, *Long John Silver, Tam O'Shanter, The Three Musketeers, Walrus and Carpenter.*

GEOFF BLOWER 1948-1967

Was apprenticed for five years under Max Henk who was his mentor. He modelled eight jugs including, *Lord Nelson, Pied Piper* and *Rip van Winkle.* He left to become a freelance and to teach. Geoff gives very amusing lectures to collectors about his days at Nile Street, of the dust and the noise, the stairs, the heavy six foot carrying boards and the wonderful characters and comradeship.

GARRY SHARPE 1953-1960

Inherited Harry Fenton's tools, who had died before he joined Doulton. Like Fenton he went to the U.S.A. to work. His work had great handle interest; *Gone Away, Old Salt; Merlin.*

DAVID BIGGS 1958-current

Worked with Max Henk developing the feature of the handle and his jugs show this very strikingly in *Jockey, Gondolier, Yachtman; Veteran Motorist; Louis Armstrong* and *Jimmy Durante.* On the introduction of the translucent china body, 1968-70 he remodelled many jugs to give the finer definition needed.

ERIC GRIFFITHS 1970-1991

Became Director of Ceramic Sculpture at Nile Street, Burslem. His style is apparent in *Henry VIII, Mark Twain, Charles Dickens* and *John Doulton,* whose complexions have none of the characteristic Fenton *scumbling.* **PETER GEE** and **ROBERT TABBENOR** joined his studio in 1973 and remain there today. Peter joined as an apprentice and concentrates on figures but his jugs include *Sir Francis Drake, Artful Dodger,* and *Catherine Howard.* Robert concentrates on jugs but his figures include *Prized Possessions* and the *Auctioneer,* both featuring character jugs. He created the *Sherlock Holmes* toby.

MICHAEL ABBERLEY also worked in the Design studio until 1983. He was responsible for the *Antagonist Collection* and also two of the double-sided *Star Crossed Lovers* series. Another was *Santa Claus* in all his forms.

In 1973 production of character jugs transferred to the Beswick factory and the Design Manager **HARRY SALES** 1961-1986, was responsible for *Mr. Quaker* and *Hampshire Cricketer* and they were modelled by **GRAHAM TONGUE** who has become Design Manager since 1986, and is responsible for the *William Grant* decanters. Harry Sales and Graham Tongue have both worked on the *Bunnykins* series and Graham Tongue's forte is in the Doulton animal range. **ALAN MASLANKOWSKI** also from the *Beswick* Design studio and normally producing animals modelled *Catherine of Aragon.*

COLIN DAVIDSON, a free-lance artist produced just one jug, *Mae West* in 1983.

DOUG TOOTLE, also a free-lance artist produced *Anne Boleyn*, **ALAN MOORE**, *The Sleuth* in 1973, and **MARTYN ALCOCK**, *Status Quo, Captain Hook* and *The Snowman* in 1993-1994.

So you see new designs can come from many sources. However at the present there are two free-lance artists who are responsible for the majority of new productions.

STAN TAYLOR

From Bristol has over 60 jugs to his name, exceeding even Harry Fenton's total.

BILL HARPER

Who was born, studied and worked in the *Potteries* all his life, but who travels far afield to meet collectors and to climb in the Himalayas for recreation has worked for Doulton since 1972. Bill is responsible for the *Doultonville Tobies, The Great Generals, The Diamond Collection* and many more beside.

BACKSTAMPS

There are some representative backstamps here, and some in the text, but the variations and combinations are almost unlimited. They give us a great deal of information and are always worth studying. The changes can be subtle. The Griffiths *Fireman* jug had only one year of production and yet in that time there were three different backstamps. The earliest is the most desirable as is often the case. When the *Three Musketeers* were first issued, *One of the Three Musketeers* was included in the backstamp but was discontinued c. 1971. *Sanco Panca's* earliest backstamp included *A Servant to Don Quixote*, which was deleted in the early 1970s. *Toby Phillpots* became *Toby Philpots* c.1952. The *Winston Churchill* toby has an early more desirable backstamp. REGD. IN AUSTRALIA was printed on many goods between c.1935and 1945, when it was introduced to protect designs being copied by the Japanese in particular.

Study your backstamps to find the earliest copies for your collection and also to add value; as for instance a *Canadian Centennial* stamp discovered can double the value of your jug. A backstamp crossed through or drilled in the centre denotes a second quality jug.

160

1934-
JOHN BARLEYCORN (large size). The first jug in the range issued in 1934 has to the right of the contemporary Lion and Crown backstamp + 13 which added to 27 gives 1940 as the date of manufacture of this particular jug. (1927-year coding system began) UK Patent Office Registration of design number 782778 issued in 1933, the year preceding production. Hand painted Doulton design number D5327 for 1933. Hand painted numbers continued until c. 1939.

1938-
PADDY Ash Bowl. Issued in 1938.
Showing + 11 which with 27 dates this ashbowl at 1938.
Registered design No. 817032 for 1936 when design of small size jug from which this model was adapted, was registered.

1938-
MICAWBER Mid size. Issued in 1938.
27 = 12 = 1939
Registered number 822825 for 1937 and added information that the design was now registered in Australia. Painter's mark.

1939-55
A mark used on some jugs manufactured between 1939 and 1955 which enabled the kiln operator to give all objects in this category the correct temperature and conditions required for this 'Georgian' type body. This mark was once a useful way of telling an early copy from an in-production model, but is losing its usefulness as most of the early jugs are now out of production.

1947-
BEEFEATERS(S) showing title in the plural. Issued in 1947 and still in production. COPR. (copyright) 1946. DOULTON & CO. LIMITED and a list of four registered design numbers. This jug also occurs with the A backstamp. Singular Beefeater came in c. 1953.

1954-
PIED PIPER Issued in 1954.
D6403 (factory design number for 1953) COPR. 1953 DOULTON & CO. LIMITED.
Between 1968-71 some character jugs were produced in a fine china body. These are slightly smaller in size due to the different shrinkage factor of this type of ware – in the large size about 1 in.

1971 -
JOCKEY. Issued in 1971.
D6625 COPR. 1970 DOULTON & CO. LIMITED. List of four registered design numbers.

1982-
SANTA CLAUS II. Issued in 1982 with Reindeer handle.
New copyright stamp ROYAL DOULTON TABLEWARE LTD. 1982. Title in new style script. Design number 6675.

CANCELLED TITLES AND SIZES

Sometimes proposed jugs are cancelled at a late stage. This happened with the *Cabinet Maker* when the *Williamsburg Collection* was discontinued in 1983. It had already been announced by Royal Doulton in 1981 that it was to be added to the set. A small size *Jockey* was piloted in 1974 but then the large size was discontinued in 1975. The same thing happened with the miniature size *Trapper* and *Lumberjack* when a large batch had already been made and they were sold off to lucky collectors in 1983.

CLUBS

Royal Doulton runs its own International Collectors Club and its magazine, *Gallery,* devotes a section to Character Jug News in each quarterly issue. There is also a *For Sale* and *Wanted* supplement for collectors. All over the world you will find local chapters of the *R.D.I.C.C.* where you can meet other jug collectors. There are other independent groups but the best established and thriving one is the CHARACTER AND TOBY JUG COLLECTORS SOCIETY OF AUSTRALIA which has published its monthly newsletter since 1980. For their tenth anniversary they produced their commemorative character jug of their patron, *John Shorter*, their address is: P.O. Box R94, Royal Exchange, Sydney, N.S.W. 2000, Australia.

CURRENT PRICES

There are many character jug price guides available in both the U.S.A., Canada, and U.K. A price guide is what it states – only a guide to what the jugs have changed hands at in various circumstances. You can get a good idea of current prices on the secondary market by collecting and comparing dealers price lists, either those in your local antiques markets or at national Doulton collectors fairs. Auction catalogues can be a useful guide too if you are able to view the lots before the sale. Remember a seemingly low price in an auction report may have been for a damaged item.

EARLY COPIES

The advantage of owning an early version of a jug rather than a later one lies in the fact that the quality of the early jug will be better. Before the Second World War labour was cheap and more time was devoted to detail. The names on the reverse were carefully picked out in a contrasting colour, e.g. the purple on the red *Cardinal's* vestment. Much more shading of colours was employed and the inside rim of the jug was sprayed with a basic colour, a practice discontinued c. 1959. The eyes were indented and moulded in relief, until c. 1958, giving them much more expression than with the later painted ones. So always collect the earliest examples you can find with marks such as 1 to 3 if the jug was first issued in the 1930s. With the later issues the *A* mark becomes a consideration and with jugs issued after 1955 choose the example which pleases you most. Jugs are still almost wholly hand painted today and there is a variation in different painters' work. On an off-day a painter has even been known to reverse the colours on the *Jester's* headress for instance. These variations are interesting but not essential to a collection.

EARLY TINIES

Early examples of the Tinies produced at the start of the Second World War had the name of the character printed on the base. The first six tinies produced in 1940, D6142 to D6147 can be found with the title. As with most pre-war products they are much more carefully painted and therefore desirable examples. Tinies were sold for 2/6d. (12.5p) in 1957.

DEVELOPMENT OF THE CHARACTER AND TOBY JUG

1820's   *Lord Nelson* jug by Doulton & Watts at Lambeth.

1910   Leslie Harradine face jugs produced at Lambeth.

1919   *Charlie* toby produced at Burslem.

1925   Harry Simeon *Toby Wares* produced at Lambeth.

1934   Charles Noke introduced the Burslem range with *John Barleycorn*.

1935   First small size jug produced, *Sairey Gamp*. Face jugs became known as *Character* jugs.

1936   Aerographed borders introduced to large and small sizes. Ashtrays, bookends and napkin rings introduced.

1937   Music jugs and tobacco jars introduced.

1938   Six Mid-size Dickens jugs introduced. Ashbowls introduced.

1939   First Toby (full length) jugs introduced into range. *Old Charley*. First teapots, sugar bowls and jug sets introduced.
A mark introduced – 1955.
Maori pilot produced.
Hatless Drake for sale in shops.
Second World War began.

1940   *Drake*, with hat, small size issued. First six tinies introduced.
White Churchill issued.
Wall vases and toothpicks introduced.

1941   *Pearly Boy* and *Pearly Girl* issued. The manufacture of all forms of decorated china for the home market prohibited. No restrictions on Export ware.

1947-   Many mould changes from remodelling after war years.

1952   Decline in exports led restrictions to be lifted on some decorated china being sold on home market.

1956   *The Musketeers* – the first *set* introduced.

1958   Table lighters introduced. Eyes no longer indented.

1960   30 jugs withdrawn.

1967-9   12 more jugs withdrawn.

1968-73 New ceramic body used, translucent china, which required remodelling of some of the jugs to give finer detail. They were painted under-glaze and became 1" smaller with 19% shrinkage as opposed to the 12.5% of earthenware.

1968-70 Texture effect added. A sort of sponged-speckle.

1973   Production transferred to *Beswick*, Longton. Earthenware body resumed.

1982   Backstamp incorporating *Handmade* and *Handpainted*.

1983   *Shakesperian Collection* introduced at higher price than large jugs in the general range.

1984   Facsimile signatures of the artists appear on the backstamp.
Mr. Quaker.

1991   Over 90 Character and Toby jugs discontinued.

1991   *Character Jug of the Year* introduced.

1992   First three-handled tyg. *Charles I*.

LATER ADAPTATIONS

Sometimes things get to quite a late stage before it is realised that a lot of witches' noses in the prototype version of the *Macbeth* jug will be damaged in manufacture and transit. In the case of the *Anne of Cleves* jug, first batches were retailed before it was realised how vulnerable the horse's ears were and a change was made. It is common sense to improve design and minimise damage.

Of course many changes are made to bring down costs in manufacture as labour becomes more expensive through the years. This has happened throughout the history of the range. Highlighted titles and details on the early copies of *John Peel, Beefeater, Cardinal*, etc. were discontinued c. 1949 and airbrushed rims in about 1959 – all to save the painters time. *Henry V's* standard and the *London Bobby's* badge were originally embossed but later changed to the transfer method for clarity and ease. We don't like our traditional jugs to respond to modern methods but that is progress. New techniques and finishes have to be used. It is why Royal Doulton prospers.

MIS-NUMBERING

D numbers often become transferred onto the wrong jug or the wrong size particularly. Sometimes the title too. The only characters to have been given the same number in error are *Bahamas Policeman* and *The Snake Charmer*.

PAINTER'S ERRORS AND PART-DECORATED ITEMS

Painters are given a pattern to match and even the strength of colour is set down, but we all have off-days when the concentration lapses. It must be easy to start the dark and light stripes on the *Falconer's* hat in the wrong order when one gets tired. These variations, whilst they add interest, I don't think they add monetary value, but then I have never understood why the white factory rejects should bring more than a perfectly finished copy. Sometimes the production of the jug is halted after only one or two colours have been applied because a pinhole or fault was discovered at a late stage.

PILOT JUGS

These are prototype jugs produced in the Doulton Studios and never put into production. Often several were made in order that they might be 'piloted' sent to Doulton companies abroad for their approval; For instance, a *Maori* jug was sent, just prior to the outbreak of the Second World War, to the Australian agents (John Shorter Pty. Limited) with the instructions to Mr. Shorter to retain it for the duration. After the War this jug was never put into production. Other jugs piloted – *Baseball Player. Jockey* small.

PRODUCTION RUNS

Sairey Gamp D5451 was in production for fifty-one years from 1935-1986 and so had a longer production run than any other jug. Today many jugs have only one year of issue but this can still result in a high figure as production is so intense compared with former times. *Old Charley* is the character that occurs in the greatest number of sizes and derivatives.

PROTOTYPES

These are jugs modelled and cast as possible issues but then rejected at a very early stage. This can be due to features which would make them too expensive when jugs were produced to a standard price, e.g. *Pilgrim Father*. When copyright release could not be obtained, e.g. *Humphrey Bogart*. When the commissioner found raising the funds required to launch your own jug too difficult e.g. *Prison Officer*. I have included a sprinkling of these jugs in the list for those who are interested. However as the only collectors who can afford them have to be millionaires and as usually only one copy exists it leaves a lot of my readers without a chance to acquire one. However, they can console themselves with the thought that the jugs are almost all stolen property and belong to Royal Doulton. Although in recent years they have been clearly marked as the factories property and not for resale 'escapes' still regularly occur, mainly to North America. In my opinion 'prototypes' are very open to abuse, having colour and backstamps added after they have left the factory. New colourways can be created outside the factory for a few pounds. So collectors can comfort themselves in realising they are not always a good investment, especially if Royal Doulton one day decide to claim them all back!

PUBLICATIONS

Character jugs are by far the most popular field of collecting amongst the Doulton productions and there are a wealth of publications to encourage the enthusiasm.

From time to time Royal Doulton have published Collectors Books of their current productions and the early editions of these have themselves become collectors' items. Some include an interesting section featuring their designers and the collector can read *How a character jug is made*.

In 1955 Royal Doulton published a collectors book *Good Sir Toby* by Desmond Eyles, now a very rare find; it told the story of the toby and its origins.

In 1976 the first booklet showing the range of discontinued character jugs *Doulton Character Jugs* was published by Richard Dennis and in 1979 this was enlarged and extended to include the tobies, rarities and derivatives by Doulton in a hardback *Royal Doulton Character and Toby Jugs by Desmond Eyles*.

There are numerous books, including this, where you can read about new issues and other interesting details. Club newsletters already mentioned are a good source of information. COLLECTING DOULTON a bi-monthly magazine has news of character jugs and also free *Wanted* and *For Sale* columns, where collectors can buy and sell.

RARE VARIATIONS

Most of these variations seem to have occured in jugs whose manufacture was interrupted by the Second World War. They are commonly known by their most distinctive difference from the standard issue but, in fact they were cast from quite different moulds.

The *Granny* without a tooth has a much simpler wimple, whilst one of the most noticeable variations in the *Cavalier* is the feather. *Old King Cole* with a yellow crown had a colour change in 1939, although the mould didn't change until 1940. That is the year when production ceased on these models and they were in a more usual guise when they appeared again after the war.

Small size *Cavaliers* which have sprouted beards and small and large size *Granny* jugs which have had a very fine dentistry job done on them are regularly seen in the salerooms!

SIZES

In the early Collectors Books the average size of character jugs are given as:
Large 5.25 in; Small 3.25 in;
Miniature 2.25 in; Tiny 1.25 in
These sizes have increased through the years until an average size is
Large 7.25 in (18 cm); Small 4.25 in (10.cm);
Miniature 2.75 in (7 cm); Tiny 1.5 in (4 cm).
e.g. *Old Charley* D5420 issued in 1934 is
5 in high.

The Fireman D6697 issued in 1983 is 7 in high.
However, recent issues, such as the *Chelsea Pensioner* D6817 1989 and *Bonnie Prince Charlie* D6858 1990 seem to be reversing this trend.
A change of scale is difficult for a collection as uniformity of size does display better.

SPECIAL COMMISSIONS

These were relatively rare until recently – but in the last nine years since the original edition of this book there have been a plethora, so that at times collectors have become confused. The commissioning of original designs such as *Mr. Quaker, Little Mester, The Collecting World* series and *The Great Generals* is always popular. However in 1985-87 Doulton took a step which is very unpopular with collectors by re-issuing discontinued characters. The *Old Charley and Mad Hatter* for Higbee and the *Sairey Gamp* for Strawbridge and Clothier were in new colourways, but the action was viewed with the same misgivings as when in 1978 Michael Abberley remodelled the original 1934 *John Barleycorn* for Michael Doulton events. In these same years, character jugs in current production were given new colourways. As with *Long John Silver* for Holmes and *Falstaff* for U.K. Fairs, both in 1987. Some were quite successful; but we did get two versions of one title, The *Falconer*, for two different retailers, Peter Jones of the U.K. and Joseph Horne of the U.S.A. 1987.

The year 1988 saw the same character, *Chelsea Pensioner*, commissioned by four different U.S. retailers in a small limited edition of 250 each before being issued in the general range. This last offers the maximum in frustration to collectors, for with such a small issue the value is immediately inflated beyond anything which should be expected for just a backstamp.

This practice continues and I have already aired my frustrations in *Yeoman of the Guard*. Special commissions sometimes appear in editions of 1,000 e.g. *General Eisenhower*. As Doulton have relaxed their regulation of a minimum of 5,000.

Special commissions and special backstamps outnumber the general range in the 1990s. This continuous demand keep modellers busy and provides the collector with a wide choice.

WHITE VERSIONS

With the exception of *Churchill,* the white glazed *McCallum,* and *Pick-Kwik* productions, all white jugs are factory rejects. This fact will be born out by the flaws which can be discovered somewhere on the body which caused them to be rejected by factory quality control at an early stage. White versions can be found of present productions but they become rarer as the Doulton factory discourages these escapes. These white versions are not wartime productions, as has been stated. The economy restriction forbidding decoration was applied to tableware for the home market only and jugs produced 1942-52 were coloured in the usual way but were 'For Export Only'. Production of such luxury goods was much curtailed during these years.

INDEX OF TITLES

In this index the key word is often the surname as titles and christian names play a second role eg John Barleycorn, Vice Admiral Lord Nelson. Adjectives however take precedence eg Bonnie Prince Charlie, Old King Cole.

Doultonville tobies are not listed individually.

Captain Ahab	1	Catherine of Aragon	59
Airman	33,34	Aramis	85
Aladdins Genie	49	'Ard of Earing	6
Alice In Wonderland	18,78	Louis Armstrong	20
American Express	1	A.R.P. Warden	62
American Collectors Society	29	'Arriet	7
Angler	1	'Arry	8
Santa Anna & Davy Crockett	4	D'Artagnan	85
Antagonists Collection	2	King Arthur & Guinevere	119
Antique Dealer	71	Artists	157-9
Antony & Cleopatra	118	Ashbowls	151
Apothecary of Williamburg	135	Ash Trays	151
Johnny Appleseed	6	Asprey & Co	148

Athos	85	Winston Churchill	26,27,63,159
Auctioneer	71	City Gent	28
Auld Mac	9	Santa Claus	28,29
Auxillary Fireman	62	Mrs Claus	29
Bacchus	9	Anne of Cleeves	60
Backstamps	160	Cleveland Flux	149
Bahamas Policeman	10	Clown	30,145
John Barleycorn	1,10,39	Clubs	112,161
Baseball Player	11	King & Queen of Clubs	145
Beatles	12	Uncle Tom Cobleigh	31
Beefeater	13,139	Colemans	31
Bentalls	13	Collecting World	71
The Best Is Not Too Good	142	Collector	71
Blacksmith Of Williamsburg	135	Christopher Columbus	32
Captain Bligh	14	Comrades In Arms	33
Humphrey Bogart	23	Capt. Cook – Pickwick	96
Anne Boleyn	59	Oliver Cromwell	25
Bookends	151	Robinson Crusoe	35
Bootmaker of Williamsburg	136	Capn. Cuttle	35
Bowls Player	14	Darley & Son	35
British Toby	15,34,47,104	Derivatives	151
Parson Brown	15	Diamond Collection	36
Buffalo Bill	15	King & Queen of Diamonds	145
John Bull – Pickwick	96	Charles Dickens	36
Busker	16	Dickens Tinies	37
Busts	152	DickensTobies	144
Buz Fuz	16	Dillards	38
Sgt Buz Fuz – Pickwick	96	Sir Henry Doulton	39
Cabinet Maker	137	John Doulton	38
Cable Value Network	29	Michael Doulton	39
Canadian Airman, Sailor & Soldier	34	Doultonville Tobies	146,147,159
Canadian Centenial	16	Sir Frances Drake	40,41,56,143
Canadian Assoc Of Art & Coll. Show	17	Jimmy Durante	21
Cardinal	17	Early Set Of Tinies	161
Lewis Carroll	18	Wyatt Earp	134
Cavalier	18	King Edward VII	41
Celebrity Collection	19	General Eisenhower	126
Char. & Toby Jug Coll. Soc. of Aus.	112,161	Elephant Trainer	42
Character Jug of The Year	24	Elf	42
Charlie – Toby	141	Queen Elizabeth/King Phillip	72
Charlie Chaplin	24,141	Engine Driver	72
Kings Charles 1	25	E.P.C.O.T.	42,47
Charrington & Co. Ltd.	148	Falconer	43,66,70
Chelsea Pensioner	26,64	Falstaff	43,125
Father Christmas –Toby	146	Fantom Music	120

Farmer John	69	
Father Xmas	145	
Fat Boy	44	
Guy Fawkes	44	
W.C. Fields	1,19	
Fireman	45,72	
Football Supporter	45	
Fortune Teller	46	
Terry Fox	47	
Kevin Francis	71	
Benjamin Franklin	47	
Clark Gable	22	
Sairey Gamp	48	
Gaoler Of Williamsburg	136	
Gardener	48,49	
Genie	49	
St. George	50	
Geronimo	133,134	
Gift Boxes	156	
Toby Gillette	50	
John Gilpin	51	
Gladiator	51	
Gladstone Pottery Museum	52	
Golfer	52,114	
Gondalier	53	
Gone Away	54	
General Gordon	125,126	
W.G. Grace	54	
Graduate	55	
Granny	55	
Grant & Lee	2	
William Grant	150	
Griffiths Pottery House	45	
Guardesman	56	
Guild of Specialist China-Glass Retailers	56	
Gulliver	57	
Gunsmith of Williamsburg	136	
Hamlet	107	
Hampshire Cricketer	57	
Happy John	142	
Henry V	109	
Henry VIII & His Six Wives	58	
King Henry VIII	58	
Heroes of The Blitz	62	
Heroic Leaders	63,72	
Wild Bill Hickock	134	
Higbee Company	64	
Highwayman – Lambeth	124,157	
Doc. Holliday	134	
D.H. Holmes	64	
Sherlock Holmes	143	
Home Guard	62	
Home Shopping Network	29	
Honest Measure	142	
Robin Hood	65	
Captain Hook	66	
Joseph Horne	66	
Catherine Howard	61	
Huntsman	iv,143	
Sir Leonard Hutton	67,72	
Jarge	67	
Thomas Jefferson	68	
Jester	68,145	
Jockey	69	
Farmer John	69	
Samual Johnson	70	
Jolly Toby	143	
Peter Jones	43,70,85	
Journey Through Britain	72	
Juggler	71	
Kevin Francis	71	
Lawleys By Post	72	
Lawyer	73	
Leprechaun	73,145	
Abraham Lincoln	74	
Little Mester	114	
Lobster Man	74	
London Bobby	75	
Lord Mayor of London	75	
Long John Silver	64,76	
Lumberjack	16,76	
Macbeth	109	
D. & J. McCallum	77	
Mad Hatter	64,77	
Man On A Barrel – Lambeth	iii	
Maori	78,163	
March Hare	78	
Groucho Marx	21	
Master	79	
Mephistopheles	v,79	

Merlin	80	Pied Piper	97
Mr Micawber	80	Pilgrim Father	97
Mikado	81	Pilot Jugs	163
Glen Miller	81	Piper	97,98
Mine Host	82	Playing Cards	146
Marilyn Monroe	23	Poacher	98
Monty	82	Policeman	72
Montgomery of Alamein	63,83	Porthos	85
Sir Thomas More	83	Postman	72
Captain Henry Morgan	84	Presidential Series	68,74,98
Earl Mountbatten of Burma	84	Elvis Presley	23
Musical Jugs	152,153	Pride & Joy	104
Musketeers	85,159	Prison Officer	99
Napkin Rings	153	Production Runs	163
Napoleon	86	Prototypes	163
Napoleon & Josephine	119	Punch & Judy	99
Nelson Lambeth	iii,87	Punch & Judy Man	100
Lord Nelson	87,88,104	Publications	164
Vice Admiral Lord Nelson	88	Quaker Oats Ltd.	100,101
Neptune	89	Mr Quaker	100
Night Watchman of Williamsburg	137	Don Quixote	101,159
North American Indian	16,89,90,114	Rare Variations	164
Annie Oakley	134	Ronald Reagan	103
Okoboji	90	Red Queen	102
Old Charley	64,90	Regency Beau	102
Old King Cole	91,64,104,158	Republican National Commitee	103
Old Mr Turveydrop – Pickwick	96	Ringmaster	104
Old Salt	92	George Robey	141
On Guard For Thee	34	Romeo	108
Othello	108	Theodore Roosevelt	98,158
Paddy	92,163	R.D.I.C.C.	38,104,145
Sancho Pança	93	Albert Sagger	145
Catherine Parr	61	Sailor	33,34
Pascoe & Co.	93,128	Salt River Cement Co.	105
Pearly Boy	8	Uncle Sam – Pickwick	96
Pearly Girl	7	Samson & Delilah	119
Pearly King	93	Samurai Warrior – Pickwick	96
Pearly Queen	93	Scaramouche	56,105,106
Pecksniff – Lambeth	iii,158	Scarlet Pimpernel	106
John Peel	94	Seaway China Co.	29,106
Pendle Witch	71,94	Jane Seymour	60
Phillip II	72	William Shakespeare	107,110
Toby Philpotts	95,159	Shakespearean Collection	107
Mr Pickwick	72,95,96,164	Bill Shankly	111
Pickwick Collection	96	Tam O' Shanter	111

Sheffield Wednesday	114	Trapper	16,122
John Shorter	112	Pierre Trudeau	122
Long John Silver	76	Friar Tuck	123
Simon The Cellarer	113	Dick Turpin	123
Simple Simon	113	Mark Twain	124
John Sinclair	52,89,114,137	Ugly Duchess	124
Site of The Green	73,115	U.K. Fairs & International Ceramics	125
Chief Sitting Bull & Custer	3	Veteran Motorist	127
Sizes	164	Vicar of Bray	127
Sleuth	72,115	Queen Victoria	56,128
Smuggler	116	Viking	128
Smuts	116	Village Blacksmith	128
Snake Charmer	117	Walklate Ltd.	150
Snooker Player	117	Wall Vases	157
Snowman	117	Walrus & Carpenter	129
Soldier	33,34	Izaac Walton	129,130
Special Commissions	165	George Washington	130
Squire	v,143	George Washington & George III	5
Star-crossed Lovers	118	Sam Weller	131
Status Quo	120	Tony Weller	131
City of Stoke-on Trent	120	Duke of Wellington	125
Strawbridge & Clothier	120	John Wesley	144
Sugar Bowls	153	Mae West	1,19
Table Lighters	153	Dick Whittington	132
Teapots	iii,105,154,155	Dick Whittington, Lord Mayor	56,132
Tinies	36,37,105,156,161	Wild West Series	134
Tobacco Jars	156	Williamsburg Collection	135-7,162
Toby Wares – Lambeth	iv,157	Rip Van Winkle	137
Toby XX	142	Witch	138
Toothpick Holders	157	Wizard	138
Town Crier	121,122,145	Yachtsman	138-9
Town Crier of Eatanswill – Pickwick	96	Yeoman Of The Guard	139,140

STOP PRESS

LATE 1994 RELEASES BY LAWLEYS BY POST

BILL SYKES D6981 Large.

KING CHARLES I/OLIVER CROMWELL Small. A Pair.

6 TOBY TINIES on Wooden Stand. First issued 1939.

6 KINGS & QUEENS OF THE REALM. Tinies on Wooden Stand.

All Modelled by Bill Harper. All Limited Editions of 2,500.

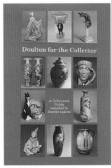

Doulton for the Collector.
Hardback, profusely illus,
27 colour pages.

£15 + £1 p & p

Doulton Flambé Animals.
Paperback, over 100 animals illus,
7 colour pages.

£3 + 50p p & p

Collecting Doulton Kingsware.
Hardback, 100 flasks in colour,
plus many other Kingsware items.

£12 + £1 p & p

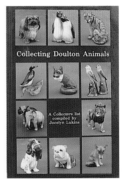

Collecting Doulton Animals.
Hardback, 300 animals illus,
10 colour pages.

£12 + £1 p & p

Doulton Burslem Advertising Wares.
Paperback, 200 items illus.

£6 + 50p p & p

Doulton Lambeth Advertising Wares.
Hardback, 300 B&W illus,
10 colour pages.

£15 + £1 p & p

Collecting Doulton Character & Toby Jugs. Hardback.
Every Jug in colour £18 + £1 p & p
For annual supplement to this book send S.A.E.
All available from **JOCELYN LUKINS, 14 KEITH GROVE, LONDON W12 9EZ**
Also sales lists of Figurines, Character Jugs, Advertising Wares etc.